IMAGES OF LINCOLNSHIRE FARMING

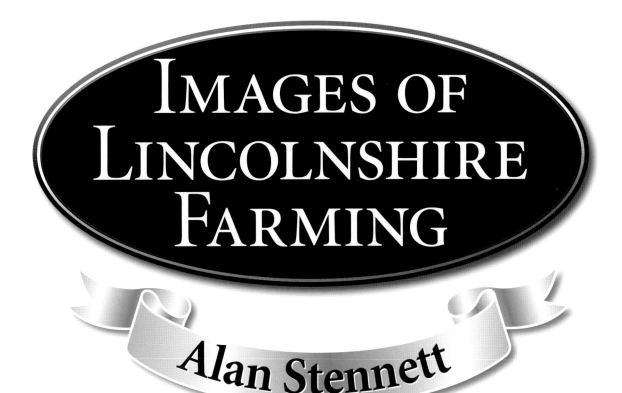

IMAGES OF LINCOLNSHIRE FARMING

Alan Stennett

COUNTRYSIDE BOOKS
NEWBURY BERKSHIRE

First published 2011
© Alan Stennett 2011

COUNTRYSIDE BOOKS
3 Catherine Road
Newbury, Berkshire

To view our complete range of books,
please visit us at
www.countrysidebooks.co.uk

ISBN 978 1 84674 258 3

Designed by Peter Davies, Nautilus Design
Produced through MRM Associates Ltd., Reading
Printed by Information Press, Oxford

CONTENTS

■

Introduction

■

WHILE RESEARCHING MATERIAL FOR *Memories of Lincolnshire Farming*, I was fortunate enough to be offered many more photographs than I was able to include in the book. Other pictures were offered later in response to it being published. Of the ones that I had in hand, some duplicated topics that were already covered. Others were not directly pertinent to the attempt to maintain the theme of the changes in farming over the years, but were still of great relevance to the farming community and anyone else with an interest in Lincolnshire agriculture and the different ways it has been carried out over the years.

Countryside Books have been kind enough to give me the opportunity to add this second volume, which allows me to make use of some of those images and to look at how individuals, families and farming businesses have had to change their working practices to meet the new demands and opportunities that the changing nature of farming has offered. I have concentrated on the period of the biggest changes – the middle third of the 20th century – because that was when the pace of change was at its greatest, although there are a number of pictures that fall outside that envelope where major changes began early or continued towards the present day.

Alan Stennett

■

■ *A Massey 726 combine owned by Geoff Hyde, leading David Creasey's Allis Chalmers Gleaner – see chapter 10 – driven by Peter Chubbuck on the Creasey farm at Hanthorpe in the late 1960s. The two combines worked together on both farms, and Geoff's wet grain was all dried in sacks.* (David Creasey) ■

THE FARM

●

MOST LINCOLNSHIRE FARMS ARE, and always have been, made up of the land, a house and some buildings: typically including a barn or barns; stock housing such as cattle yards, pig sties and stables; and cart hovels or other equipment stores. Some might be distributed round the farm in convenient locations, but most are usually gathered together, possibly with the house itself, to form a single unit, or farmstead. The buildings themselves, and the layout of the farmstead, have always changed over time. Susannah Wade Martins, in her *Historic Farm Buildings* suggests that prior to the mid-19th century few farmsteads, other than those of major estates, had a planned layout. She quotes one earlier source as saying that they were

■ *The traditional farmyard. Ada Brinkley feeding chickens at Frampton West in the 1930s.*
(From the Museum of Lincolnshire Life, courtesy of Lincolnshire County Council.) ■

■ *Witham View Farm on Timberland Fen, probably taken in the 1960s. The main block of farm buildings appears to be in traditional use, with cattle in the crew yard. A Dutch barn seems to have been added fairly recently, judging by the roof and the fresh concrete footing to the uprights, but stacks are still being built in the stackyard, with an elevator reaching up from the barn. The other building in the stackyard looks to have been built of concrete breeze blocks. (Sam Leggate)* ■

■ *A farmyard near Woodhall Spa during threshing of what looks like rye. The waggon is backed up to the barn in which the threshing is taking place. Two horses on a gin are providing the motive power for the mechanisms inside. As the horses walk round, they turn a shaft which drives the belt going into the barn.* (John Wield, courtesy of Woodhall Spa Cottage Museum.) ■

built 'without order or method … accumulated over the generations', while another, writing in 1843, noted the buildings' 'ill-arranged and patchwork appearance'.

That description probably continued to be an accurate one for many smaller farms. The first farm I remember, at Billingborough, simply had a line of wooden sheds, brick pig-sties and a brick boiler-house, in which potatoes and swill were cooked up for the pigs. To these, my father added a brick slaughter house for his butchery business, a crewyard built of railway sleepers and corrugated iron, and a corrugated iron shed to house the farm lorry.

In the late 1930s, Reg Dobbs' father's 100-acre farm near Pinchbeck included two yards, one of which had a stable for five horses, and a brick and tile barn which housed everything from mangolds for the cattle and horses, through bought-in bagged feed for pigs and poultry, to their own bagged barley meal, ground in the local mill, as pig feed. There was a similar crewyard to the one my father built and what Reg described as 'fenland outhouses'. These were constructed of timber and corrugated iron, and housed pigs, a couple of cows and a store of cut oat sheaves for horse feed.

It should be added, though, that many of the farms built for council tenancies and other deliberate attempts to open farming to more small producers were often well-designed with a house and a small range of buildings. Witham View Farm on Timberland Fen had a house and a neat open-ended square of buildings, including the barn round a crewyard which housed cows and pigs. A line of stables, tack rooms and other facilities lay to one side. John Michael's farm at North Somercotes is almost exactly as it was when it was built in the 1860s. He describes it thus:

'It's what I would call a two-horse farm. A house with a cat-slide roof [one with one side longer than the other, extending out over a single storey extension], a two-bay cart shed with a granary over and a barn with a stable for the horses next to it. The kitchen garden is exactly half an acre, and it would have been regarded as an integral part of the farming unit. At about 150 acres it was a typical Marsh unit, and I have deliberately kept it as close to that as I can.'

Larger premises, however, were often laid out in a more formal style. The farm on which I spent my teenage years included many of the typical elements. The house itself, including domestic stores, a cheese room and sleeping space for a number of employees, formed the north side of a square, surrounding a crew yard for livestock. Along the east side, next to the house, was a well, adjacent to which, rather worryingly, was a pig sty, then a large barn with a covered cattle shed running along the side facing into the square. The barn comprised a large, tall, central space for straw or hay storage, two more pig sties on the north end and a granary with cattle housing under the south end. The single storey west side of the square included loose boxes, stables and a tack, or harness, room, while the two-storey south incorporated more livestock spaces, and a feed room on the ground level, with what was probably a hay loft and a dovecot above them. A wagon hovel faced out onto the stackyard to the south of the main structure. Other farms would not have been identical, but would have included many of the same components.

Over the years elements of this pattern became less relevant, or just inadequate for the farm's needs. Barns and granaries became too small to store the crops; cart hovels were too low or too shallow from front to back to allow tractors and modern equipment to be kept there; stables and tack rooms lost their function as horses left the farms and individual sties were no longer needed as the habit of keeping a pig to kill for the winter declined.

Buildings sometimes lent themselves to change. On my father's farm the loose boxes, stables and stock housing became milking parlours and a dairy, while the tack room housed the motor that drove the vacuum milking pumps. The cart hovel did accommodate our first little grey Ferguson tractor and the limited range of equipment needed at that time to run a small dairy farm but, in the end, it succumbed to being a store for odds and ends that might come in useful at some time. Many a modern tractor restoration project has been born from the old machine left in a corner of a shed that was never needed for a more useful purpose! Most recently, the farm has now been taken over by my nephew as a stables and riding school, with the buildings used by my brother and his wife for a café and business units.

Many farms moved from general mixed farming to a more specialist

In 1967 Harold Russell took the tenancy of Scottlethorpe Grange Farm at Edenham, near Bourne. He immediately had constructed a 600-ton, on-floor grain store, with integral drying up through the floor. 'It was big and expensive, but it more than paid its way,' he says.
(Harold Russell) ■

sector, sometimes changing again as circumstances altered. A classic smaller farm example would be Lowfields Farm at Bardney, a medium-sized mixed farm in the 1920s. At that stage it had all the typical elements of such a holding: a house, alongside a crew yard surrounded by stables and a chaff house; a barn with an upper level granary; a wagon hovel; and one or two other smaller sheds and enclosures. When George White took over the farm he milked cows in what had been the stables before adding the first new building, a milking shed for 40 cows with individual standings and machine milking unit. George's son, Peter, explained,

'He was really ahead of his time – there was no power or mains water there, so he put in an engine for the milking unit and a pump to draw up water, with a big boiler in one of the sheds to heat water for washing the equipment.'

A silage pit was added – after early experiments with a self-assembly cylindrical silo had been tried. The crew yard and the cart hovel were eventually demolished, the stables had their roofs raised and the granary was stripped out of the barn to allow greater headroom, and larger doors were fitted to improve access for more modern equipment.

When Peter took over, the milking herd increased to 70 animals, and two large open-span buildings were added to house them. By the mid 1970s, it had become apparent that small-scale dairying was no longer economic, so the farmer went over to arable crops, converting the large sheds into a grain store. It was a big change for anyone farming on that heavy land, and it only became practical as larger machinery became available to do the cultivation.

'The land around here always used to be dairy and beef – at one time you could go from here to Bucknall [about 3

■ *Lowfields Farm, Bardney, today. The original brick buildings are at the far right of the complex, with the milking parlour below it. The later cattle sheds/grain store are the large buildings on the right. The brick building, top centre, is a recent addition where the rest of the crew yard would have been, and the remains of the silage pit can be seen at the upper left.* (Author) ■

miles away] and see nothing but cattle, but once you could handle it, it was alright as arable.'

In recent years, the land was always worked by contractors, but is now mostly in environmental schemes, with the buildings used for storage.

Putting up additional larger buildings or modifying existing ones to provide the space and facilities needed on the changing farm was a regular way of modernising.

'We took off the roofs round the old yard, knocked down the interior walls and put a big asbestos roof over the whole lot for a new big yard.' [Graham Parkinson]

■ *Lincoln Red cattle housed in an open yard, with access to cover.* (Author's collection) ■

Open-sided Dutch barns became more common as farmers needed to store more hay and straw, often in bales, and to keep it dry, although the silage pit often replaced the need to make hay at all. Grain silos, stores and driers popped up on many farms, and large multi-purpose buildings were able to house machinery or animals, store crops or act as packing or processing centres. Livestock, particularly pigs and poultry, moved into purpose-built premises; sheep came indoors in the winter for the first time and dairy cattle got used to bigger, more automated milking parlours.

As Lincolnshire moved away from being a mixed farming area, the outlying yards and buildings often fell into disuse or, more recently, were sold off for conversion into houses. The same has also happened to farm houses and cottages that became surplus to requirements when holdings were amalgamated into bigger farms. Whole farmyards in villages have also often been sold off for development when no room was available for expansion, or where non-farming villagers complained about the sounds and smells of agricultural activity.

■ *Drove Farm on Martin Fen in the 1970s. Traditional buildings can still be seen on both sides of the road across the fen, with additional larger structures on the 'lower' yard. The buildings by the house have now gone, and the traditional ones across the road have either been demolished or converted into two houses.* (John Harrison) ■

■ *A 1778 Dutch barn at Fillingham Castle being filled with straw bales in the 1970s.*
(From the Museum of Lincolnshire Life, courtesy of Lincolnshire County Council.) ■

HARD LABOUR

MOST FARMERS AND FARM WORKERS today would, quite correctly, say that they work hard, but there is no doubt that the hard physical labour of a few decades ago has largely gone. Nobody is now expected to heave sacks containing 16 stone of

barley, 18 of wheat, or even more of peas or beans, let alone carry them up the steps to a granary. A day's ploughing no longer means getting up in the dark, preparing a horse, hitching it to a plough, then walking behind it for somewhere between ten and twenty miles depending on the width of the furrow.

Many other farm jobs were physically hard work too. In those pre-herbicide days, virtually every crop needed weeding, at least in its early stages. Cereal crops would be harrowed to remove small weeds early in the season, but would then be horse or tractor hoed between the rows of the growing crop. Hand-hoeing also played its part. Wild oats would be rogued by hand, and troublesome individual weeds such as thistles and docks taken out with either a sharp thistle hook that chopped through its stem or a dock iron that cut through the root of the plant. Turnips, mangolds, swedes and other root crops for stock feed had to be gapped and singled – jobs that involved many hours of bent backs over a hoe or even crawling in the fields to get the right spacing for the optimum yield.

Potatoes also needed weeding, but the main hard labour elements of that crop came at the

■ *Skerrying potatoes on Ernest Wrisdale's St Cuthbert's Farm, Eastville. Maurice Taylor (aged 18) working Jolly and Tipler. (From the Museum of Lincolnshire Life, courtesy of Lincolnshire County Council.)* ■

■ *Harry Warren, farm foreman, and Sydney Rouse, Waggoner, picking potatoes at Arthur Borrill's Slate House Farm, Hibaldstow. The horse looks tired out!*
(Arthur Borrill) ■

beginning and end of the growing process. The seed potatoes would arrive on the farm in late winter or early spring, and be spread out in crates, exposed to the light, but protected against cold, to sprout or 'chit'. Once the tubers had chitted, and the ground was ready – according to one story, that was when a naked bottom could be applied to the soil without discomfort – planting could take place. The crates of chitted seed were loaded onto carts and taken to the fields, which would have been well fertilised and ridged up ready to receive it. Two workers would then take an end of a crate each and, carrying it between them, walk down the rows, placing single tubers at the required spacing, leaving a clear furrow between the two. Sometimes a third person would follow behind filling the middle row but, if not, another pair would be behind working that row and one to the side of the first two.

'You would take three potatoes in your hand and place them in the furrow at the right spacing, then step forward, swinging the crate with you. You had to get into the rhythm, it was one, two, three – swing.' [Brenda Waite]

My aunt complained that she would rather carry a basket by herself, since she could never get to move at the same time and pace as her crate partner. The middle planter could suffer even more from a bad back, since he or she had nothing to lean on while bending.

It was usually estimated that a planter could cover half an acre or a bit more in a day, but picking was a slower job, although one that still left aching backs from all the bending. The tubers would first have been ploughed out, or exposed by a potato spinner, which spread the row and its contents sideways, allowing the tubers to be picked up from the surface. The pickers worked down the spun rows filling 'skeps' (baskets) that had been left alongside. The baskets would then be picked up and the contents emptied into a cart, with the empties left alongside the next row to be lifted. A tractor driver who wanted to make life difficult for the pickers would set the spinner so that it spread the row further than was necessary.

'I had a good team of four women who worked really well when I was on the spinner, but one day one of the husbands came out instead, and he kept telling me what I should be doing, so I just set the spinner to throw his row out twice as far. He grumbled, but he took the hint.' [Terry Atkinson]

'If someone upset me, or I wanted to tease them a bit, I'd spin them out further so they had to reach out more to collect them.' [Brian Waite]

Since Brian and Brenda first met while working as a tractor driver and a potato picker, it seems as if that teasing worked for them, however frustrating it might have been for other pickers!

Where the crop was ploughed out, it was often necessary to come back for another pass with the plough, to unearth anything that had been left hidden in the turned soil. Anything left in the ground was not only a loss to the farmer, but was also a potential 'volunteer' to pop up in the following year's crop.

Some potatoes would be sold off the farm immediately, but many were stored on-farm in pies, clamps or graves, depending where in the country you were building them. The crop was piled into a long row with a triangular cross-section. This was covered with layers of straw and topped off with a covering of earth – a skilled job we will talk about more in a later chapter – which was capable of keeping the crop in good condition for many months through the winter. When the time came to open the clamps to sell or use the potatoes, the covering would be stripped away to expose as much as was wanted. The tubers would be scooped into a riddle to shake off loose soil, then tossed into a bag, held open under a metal frame which both kept the bag upright and made it easier to fill.

'There was a trick to getting the spuds straight into the bag – you had to kind of flick the riddle so they all flew together in a straight line. If you just tried to tip them in, some fell each side and missed the frame.' [Judith Bee]

On bigger farms, the riddling might be partially mechanised with the aid of a little oil engine that drove a short elevator and a sorting platform. That combined the job of riddling loose earth and small stones and providing a surface from which larger stones or damaged tubers could be removed by hand.

'Those little Lister engines were all over the place – driving mills or pumps, turning root cutters; anywhere where a bit more power was needed than manpower, or was required continuously for a long time.' [John Redhead]

Sugar beet was another crop that required a lot of bending and handling. When drilled, the crop would come up in a thick row, which had to be gapped – removing most of the plants to leave small clumps – which were then 'singled' to take them down to single plants at the right spacing.

■ *A day beet singling would leave you with a very aching back.* (Courtesy of Lincolnshire Film Archive) ■

'We were given one or more acres to gap – the farmer told us to do it at our own speed – slowly and well was better than fast but rough, although what you got paid depended on how much you did.' [Brian Waite]

'The men did the gapping, but they tried to avoid the singling. I could usually do it by bending down, but a lot of people ended up crawling down the rows, especially if your back got bad or it got very fiddly'. [Brenda Waite]

Reg Dobbs was paid seven pence a row as a boy for singling 'a very long row' for the local churchwarden, and he said he often ended up crawling down the row to ease his back. My wife thought that was generous – she got sixpence for a row 'that seemed to vanish over the horizon when you were crawling'.

When it came to harvesting or lifting beet, the crop would first be loosened in the ground with a beet plough. Men would then walk down the rows, pull up a root with each hand, bang them together to get rid of surplus soil – 'knocking' them – and then drop them on the ground. They would return with a suitable knife, chopping off the tops and leaves, and either tossing them into a cart or dropping them once

■ Dressing beans with Frank Allen's dresser during the Second World War – 'Helmut' and two Ukrainian PoWs at Grove Farm, Swaton. (Chris Richardson) ■

■ *'Mr Mardit' hoeing beet at Grove Farm, Swaton, in 1949.* (Chris Richardson) ■

again in the rows for someone to follow with the cart, collecting them as the horse moved along.

'I did ten acres every year under piece work, and your back ached after a session of that – now I see that what I did in a season, they can do in about an hour!' [John Redhead]

'My dad always said that sugar used to be produced by slave labour, and the way we had to work it still was!' [Michael Lambert]

Hay-making and harvest are probably the non-farmer's image of an idyllic summer job – all sun-bronzed lads and lasses strolling through the fields and chatting while they do a little light turning of sweet-smelling hay, or tossing a few bundles of straw up to a chap happily riding on a horse-drawn wagon. The reality, in the days of manual labour was rather different. A newly-cut swath of hay is heavy, and requires a certain knack to keep it rolling over evenly to expose another face to the drying effects of the wind and sun – always assuming that there is wind and sun. Turning a hay swath that has been rained on is no fun at all – it is even heavier, and there is the clear knowledge that the process is going to go on for some time.

Loading hay is another job where 'the knack' is essential. Loose hay does not naturally stay on the fork, and the untrained hand is likely to be covered in dry grass falling off the fork, with very little getting up to the man on the top. The arrival in the hay-field of the baler helped but, in the days before fork-lifts and front-loaders, they still needed to be heaved onto trailers and off again to make the stack.

Making sheaves, in the days when corn was cut with a reaper, again involved much bending and lifting, as well as learning the skill of making a tie out of twisted straws to go round the sheaf. The reaper-binder did away with that job, except where the knotter failed and someone had to follow on gathering up the loose material left behind; in the corners where the binder couldn't get; or the first circuit of the field, which had to be cut with scythes and tied manually to give a clear track for the binder to follow while cutting the strip alongside the machine. Even there, the sheaves themselves still needed a lot of handling. Picked up in twos, they were placed in stooks – two rows of sheaves leaning against each other with a space between for the wind to blow through to help finish the drying process. Again, it's a job that looks straightforward, but the sheaves were quite heavy – the crop was not fully dry when harvested – and the thistles and other weeds that were an inevitable part of the bundle, as well as the sharp ends of the straw, could make handling them unpleasant.

'All the inside of your arms would be red-raw after a day's stooking.' [Bob Fletcher]

On occasion the whole stook had to be moved or turned to improve the wind flow through it. You could either dismantle the stook and rebuild it, or make use of a stook lifter – a frame that lifted the whole construction without breaking it down.

The regular job of feeding housed livestock, particularly in the winter, could be hard work. Slicing mangolds or swedes in a hand-turned root cutter – a kind of giant circular cheese-grater that sliced chips off the feed roots – was hard. I remember how the handle would buck and judder as it bit into a new root and how the amount of chipped feed that came out the bottom always seemed remarkably small for the number of turns of the handle. Hay would be cut from the stack with a stack-knife – a large blade with a handle at right angles to it – then forked up as a block and carried across the yard to the beasts. The general effect was that of a small haystack with legs moving towards the stock. Bedding down required similar amounts of work carrying and spreading straw, although the stock did a fair amount of the spreading while picking over the new material for anything that looked worth eating.

A lot of seasonal farm work was done at piece-work rates – the workers were not on a regular wage, but were paid for measured amounts of work. Tying and stooking sheaves could be paid by the field; potato planting and beet gapping and singling by length of row; and muck carting by the twenty loads or at a rate per stockyard cleared.

Mucking out – the annual clearing of the accumulated manure from livestock yards or sheds was a heavy job, and one that could cost a worker dear if he took it on at a lower rate than was justified.

■ One man with a fork setting out to spread the heaps of muck dropped off from a cart – Home Farm, Long Sutton, 1955. (Peter Piccaver, courtesy of Lincolnshire Film Archive.) ■

■ Making the labour a bit less hard. Mr L. E. Gibson testing a horse-drawn Marshall muck-spreader at Bransby in 1930. (From the Museum of Lincolnshire Life, courtesy of Lincolnshire County Council.) ■

■ Girls churning butter in a competition at Sleaford organised by the Kesteven Agricultural Committee in 1925. (From the Museum of Lincolnshire Life, courtesy of Lincolnshire County Council.) ■

'You had to work out how deep it was and how wet it was before agreeing a rate, or you could get beat by the weight.'

The muck wasn't usually spread at the same time as the mucking out was done. The cart loads would be dropped off in the fields, either as a large muck-hill to 'mature' for a while, or as smaller individual heaps dropped off from the carts as they worked down a field. Muck spreading from the heaps might have been done later as piece work, but could be done by the regular men to ensure that it was completed properly. Teams of piece workers often cleared the harvest field of sheaves and passed them up onto the rick, but the stack itself was frequently built by the permanent staff of the farm, again to make sure the job wasn't spoiled by someone looking for a quick finish.

Sometimes, part of the payment would be withheld until the end of the job to make sure men didn't leave halfway through. According to Tony Piccaver, his father dreaded the job of negotiating the rates for piece work, 'He said that the men always knew what the job was worth much better than he did.'

Piece work is still practised in some jobs, particularly in the flower and vegetable parts of the county, but it began to die out after the Second World War as labour became more difficult to find. Henry Fell, working as farm manager for Clifford Nicholson in the 1950s, replaced piece labour rates with salaries for full-time employees: 'People were not willing to rely on the old system, so we had to offer salaries and full-time jobs to keep the good ones on the farm.'

Bob Scarborough felt that workers nowadays were not only not strong enough to do the jobs that they would once have taken in their stride, they were also unwilling to take the hardships that came with them:

'A lot of them, when they come from school, have to be with you for a year before they are fit enough, and they won't suffer for it. We used to get blisters on our hands, but we kept on until the blisters turned to hard skin and we just accepted it, because everybody else did it. They are not keen on that now.'

LOST ARTS

■

EVERY FARM WORKER WOULD ONCE have been expected to be a jack of all trades, but many would also have needed to be masters of skills that are rarely needed nowadays, or which have become specialised trades in their own right. Jobs like laying tile drains across a field, plashing a hedge to leave a stock-proof barrier or using a hicking stick to help a man lift a sack of potatoes or other produce would once have been almost second nature to a farm worker.

Hedging, ditching and tile-draining would have been winter jobs. Hedges were the main defence against animals straying out of fields, and they had to be kept in good order. At the most basic level that would just have been a case of trimming back excess growth, usually

■ *Clarence McCallum laying tile drains on Frank Richardson and Sons' 'The Grange' at Morton, 1940.* (Brian Lawrance) ■

■ *George Yarnell, still expert in the use of a scythe after a working life on farms at Stainfield and Morton.* (Brian Lawrance) ■

with a hedge knife – an eight to ten inch blade on the end of a three or four foot handle. Where the hedge had been left too long, with gaps appearing at the base, it would need to be relaid. The growth is first cut back and excess branches trimmed, then the main stems are plashed – partially cut through with a knife or a billhook to allow them to be bent over low down and parallel to the ground. They can then be either pegged down or twisted into an adjoining stem to hold them until new shoots sprout to thicken the whole hedge. With the reduction in livestock numbers on Lincolnshire farms, and the availability of simpler ways of keeping stock in, such as electric fences, very few hedges get properly laid nowadays, and where it is done, an expert is usually brought in to do it. Any overgrowth is usually dealt with by a tractor mounted flail.

Ditching too has changed. A man would once have mowed the banks with a scythe and cleared the bottom with a variety of specialist spades and scoops.

'If it had been left for a few years, so there was more than a foot or so of material in the bottom, what they had to do was free it up from the sides with a tool called a ritter. Next he cuts the material in the bottom into squares, and a man with a long-handled drag pulls as much as possible up the bank. A man in the bottom of the dyke then uses a tool called a slough – a kind of wooden spade with a sharp edge to cut roots and the like – to do the final clearance and shaping on the bottom. Any crumbs that were left were taken out with a crowle.' (Bob Unsworth)

All that range of jobs done by men and tools has now been replaced by a one-man operated tractor with mounted mowers and backhoes.

Powered mole-drainers and pipe-layers have similarly taken over from the men in the field using clay pipes, or tiles, tools like scoops, gouges and tile hooks and a knack of judging the fall of the pipe by holding back the water with sections of broken slate or tile.

'We used to start around November when the soil was dry enough to dig, but with enough water to be able to set the levels. You dig back about three yards from the dyke you're going to flow into. I

and drain away. The trench could then be refilled with soil.

'Done like that – done properly, it would last for a hundred years, as long as you kept the end open at the dyke.'

The Bomford Sapper, the Henderson trencher and the Roteho were all mechanical devices that aimed to simplify the process, and reduce the manpower, while continuing with the traditional clay tiles, although gravel rapidly replaced brushwood as the permeable layer in the trench.

That 'need to know' extended into the harvest field. Everyone with any experience knew how best to load loose hay or straw onto a wagon – 'the chap on top had to use his fork to pull the hay off what was being offered, not try to spike it with his own fork'. The same applied to a load of sheaves – rough handling could shake the grain out of the ears and

■ *Laying tile drains using a mechanical trencher. It saved the effort of digging, but lost the old precision of getting the fall exactly right across a field.* (Bob Scarborough) ■

mark the level with an old house slate. That fills the trench with water to that level. We call it taking the water with you, so that when you dig down, with the gripping tool or the gouge, if the bottom is just touching the water, you know you've got the level. You take the crumbs out with a round scoop, which is just right to lay the tiles into the groove at the bottom. The tool we lay them in with is called a tile hook which was made for you by a blacksmith. It had two hooks on it, one to hold the tile and the other so you could turn the tile if it didn't quite fit – it was sometimes better if you spun it a bit.' [John Harrison]

Brushwood, which had already been collected as a by-product of the hedging, then went in on top of the tiles to allow water to seep through

■ *Philip and George Effield using a stook lifter at Mareham le Fen in 1939. The stooks here may have been being moved to allow the undersown clover to grow on.* (From the Museum of Lincolnshire Life, courtesy of Lincolnshire County Council.) ■

■ *Peas for stockfeed being loaded near Woodhall Spa onto a Lincolnshire hermaphrodite wagon – one converted from a two-wheeled cart by adding an extra pair of wheels and racks to extend the cart area.* (John Wield, courtesy of Woodhall Spa Cottage Museum.) ■

loads poorly packed tended to slip off the waggon when being moved over rough ground or poor roads. George Curtis wrote about 'working consciously to a precise and detailed plan', which involved a careful construction of the corners of the load, then adding the 'shoulders' before filling in the middle. An additional complication was added if the wagon was a Lincolnshire hermaphrodite, or 'moffrey' where the shafts were removed from a two-wheeled cart. A fore-carriage, also two-wheeled, was attached to the front and a platform was extended from the front of the cart over the fore-carriage. With the addition of racks, or 'shelving' to the front and sides, many more sheaves could be carried than by the cart alone, but the stacking of the load, which was starting from two levels, needed more skill to get well-balanced.

Building a stack of sheaves was considered a particularly skilled job, and a farmer would often only entrust the task to his most reliable men. When Bob Scarborough built his first stack, he forgot one of the

■ *First prize-winner in the Flax Stax competition in 1946. Stack builder William Spencer, with his son-in-law Joe Ogden, a German PoW, Dennis Simpson and Dick and Reg Spooner. (From the Museum of Lincolnshire Life, courtesy of Lincolnshire County Council.)* ■

■ *A stack of wheat built and thatched at Aisby by farmer Philip Selby and a Mr Everard in 1881. The stack was not threshed until 1913, but the quality of the stack-making was such that the grain was in good condition. It was bought by Grantham corn merchants Henry Bell for stock feed, although attempts to get it to germinate failed. A sample of the wheat is still owned by the Grant family, who provided this picture of the stack. (Nikki Grant)* ■

■ *The modern art of stack-building. 'Mambo', a straw mammoth built as the winning entry in a breakfast cereal competition by the Grant family near Hubberts Bridge.*
(Paul Grant) ■

golden rules of stack building: always make sure that the outer sheaves, which are always put in with the cut ends outwards, are not allowed to creep outwards too much as the stack rises. Some outward placement is needed to get the curved side that is best for shedding rain, but Bob found that his stack got too wide too quickly, so he had to finish it low and fat, much to the amusement of his colleagues. Newcomers to the farm or workers on piece rate might not have got the stack built well enough, or make an adequate job of the thatching required on the top to keep out the weather. One old hand remembered that the stack-builder was often the foreman or waggoner, the head horse-man, with another horse-man laying the binding sheaves behind the outer layer put down by the lead man. If a 'chimney' is to be left in the stack to allow heat or moisture to rise from the crop, that could be achieved by leaving a large bag of chaff or loose straw in the bottom layer, then pulling it up as the stack is built, so leaving an open column through the structure.

The thatching itself, being the most visible part of stack-building, was a skill of which a farm-hand could be justly proud. The straw to be used for thatching had first to be drawn – selected and straightened into a neat bundle, with all the cut ends together. This bundle is then taken up onto the top of the stack and a series of them are laid all the way along the bottom edge of the sloped top. For a really professional job, it is then combed through with a small wooden rake before the next layer is applied further up the roof – the process is just like tiling a house roof, with the completed section moving up the roof towards the ridge. The ridge at the top of the structure is covered with a layer of doubled over straw. The finished thatch would then be held in place, either by a weighted net, or by lines of string running across the thatch, held in place by three-foot-long pegs. The arrival of the combine harvester to do away with the need to stack sheaves, and the baler to deal with loose hay or straw, rendered the whole business redundant, and the skills, for anyone except a professional thatcher working on buildings, went with it.

A similar lost skill is the ability to build and cover potato pies or clamps. The crop used to be stored in the field as a long ridge, triangular in cross-section, which was covered with straw, followed by a layer of earth, to keep the crop over the winter. When needed, the covering was removed and the crop was riddled to remove loose soil; any bad potatoes, stones or unwanted clods removed and the crop bagged up for sale. Another trick of the trade was the use of a hicking stick to help swing a sack up onto a lorry. Two men would each take one of the ears of the sack, put the stick under the other end and lift without having to try to grab the full bottom corners of the sack.

Tony Hutton claimed to be one of the last people in Lincolnshire to be making potato clamps:

'I couldn't get the labour, so I did it myself. Built and strawed the clamp and then graded out of it right up to the 90s, but I had to stop then because we couldn't stop them chitting. We used to have Technazine granules, but when they took that off the market, nothing else seemed to do the job.'

Tony didn't riddle the crop out of the clamp, he loaded a one-ton box from it and took it back to his own grading line.

'I could tip that box into the hopper, and from there it went onto the rods and some brushes to clean them and, as long as I ran it slowly, I could pick off anything that wasn't wanted by myself, although I did sometimes have some help from my wife.'

Some other skills needed by the farm worker in the past might not seem quite so obvious. Most would have been able to butcher a pig and, with the help of his wife, 'put it away' – cure the bacon, make sausages and pork pies and deal with all the miscellaneous odd bits of the carcase that needed turning into brawn, scraps and pigs fry. Most would also be able to do the killing, but that was often left to the local butcher or slaughterman. H. S. Goose, the appropriately-named butcher from Tattershall obviously specialised in the art, since a bill to one local farmer, Mr Willows, shows him killing 57 pigs in 1936, at a rate varying from 5/- for one pig up to £1.14s for seventeen at a time – obviously he offered a bulk discount! The same bill also reveals that he delivered 6 cwt of potatoes at a price of £1.10s, which seems a little surprising, since Mr Willows, as we will see later, grew a lot of potatoes!

■ *Loading potatoes from a clamp at Nocton. The man on the right has a hicking stick, with which he has just helped to lift the bag onto the back of the chap next to him.* (Len Woodhead) ■

■ *Building a potato grave on Arthur Borrill's Slate Farm at Hibaldstow. The potatoes have been tipped from the horse-drawn cart and are being built up into a long ridge. That ridge is then covered with the long straw seen in loose 'bats' in the foreground. The whole construction would then be covered with earth.* (Arthur Borrill) ■

In the war years and immediately post-war, when food was rationed, the slaughterman would normally be accompanied by a policeman to check that only the licensed number of pigs was killed. I can remember, as a small boy, the local bobby sitting drinking tea with us in the house while the killing went on, without paying significant attention to the numbers being done away with. Brian Waite has similar memories, 'We often killed seven on a licence for six, and the only time we saw the policeman was when he came to collect his plate of pigs fry.'

Brian also learned to sow seeds in the way that they had been distributed for centuries:

'I was working with my uncle, who was broadcasting clover seed by hand into the barley crop. We under sowed it so we could get two cuts of clover for hay, and then it was ploughed in ready for a crop of potatoes. I asked him to let me have a go, and I got so you couldn't tell the difference. It made your back and shoulders ache because it was a different way of working than we were used to. Later we got a barrow drill for the small seeds.'

Although it would not necessarily be regarded as a universal skill, except among the waggoners and garthmen – horse and cattle specialists respectively – most farm workers would also have had a working knowledge of many of the diseases and conditions that affect livestock, and know when the expensive services of a vet had to be summoned or could be left, at least for the time being. They might even extend that knowledge to human conditions, as Anthony Hopkins confirmed:

'After you've been working through the winter, and your hands get all chapped and cracked, putting fertiliser on works wonders. When you get some nitrogen on them in the spring, it stings at first, but it soon clears them up.'

I'm not sure how the health and safety police nowadays would see such a treatment, but these matters were of less concern half a century ago. Bob Scarborough was taught by his father that he should always keep his woodworking tools sharp:

'Father insisted on it – he said you can't expect a joiner to do a good job with blunt tools. You have to respect them. I learned that the hard way and have the scars to this day to prove it, but I did eventually learn to use them properly and safely.'

■ *Pigs killed and ready for butchering as part of the wages of farm workers at Hacconby, late 1940s. (l. to r.) Mr Booth, labourer; A. Carlton, waggoner; H. Wells, pig killer; Mr Goodman, farm manager; and G. Fisher, waggoner.* (Brian Lawrance) ■

FAMILIES AT WORK

FAMILIES AND FARMING ARE inextricably tied up together. Farmers' families were expected to help on the farm in their childhood and move on to full-scale farming in their own right as they grew older – although the older was often significantly older if it required the previous generation to step down before the new could take over. Very few farmers, probably throughout the history of farming, have ever been totally convinced that the next generation was ready to take control!

On the workers' side, sons following fathers was the normal state of affairs in the countryside, at least partly because of the lack of alternative employment in most rural villages. Many of the older

■ *Mr & Mrs Spendlove picking potatoes.* (Chris Richardson) ■

■ *A tea break during threshing on Poplar Farm Croft in the 1940s.* (From the Museum of Lincolnshire Life, courtesy of Lincolnshire County Council) ■

■ *The Sleaford family and friends potato riddling. From left: Mrs Grace Sleaford, with Jess and Sid; sitting, Charles and Ray Sleaford; by the riddles, Mrs Alice Cooling. The other ladies have not been identified.* (Michael Cooling) ■

farm workers I have spoken to were only too keen to escape from what they saw as the boredom of schoolwork to what they regarded as 'a man's job at a man's pay', although most of them found that they were initially expected to put in the work, but at a lower rate than older employees.

'I never thought of doing anything else, and my dad encouraged me in that – I used to go and see him every day before going off to school, and if he was droving cattle to another farm at Moorhouses, he would say "Best hide yersen until the bus has gone, then tell your mother that you have missed it and you can

■ *This family member has obviously come along to help potato pick, but she looks rather reluctant to get involved.* (Bob Scarborough) ■

come with me". I worked with him from the time I left school in 1954 until I took over from him in 1969.' [Brian Waite]

Women and girls were less likely to get directly involved. According to Joseph Smith's memories of life on the fens in the early part of the 20th century it was unusual to see women working in the fields before the First World War other than at harvest time or for odd jobs such as singling root crops or 'spudding' thistles to weed them out of grassland. The need for extra labour during that war saw many women and girls take up farm work, which he suggests continued to be preferred after the conflict to domestic service, the only other alternative open to most young women. Even so, the opportunities available to women on farms were limited. In the fields they tended to be put to what one of my contributors described as 'finicky' work – singling round individual beet plants, harvesting green peas and potato picking and planting, although that was important enough for all available labour to be put to it.

Brenda Waite saw doing whatever work was going as being important to the family economy, 'There were seven of us at home, so we had to go out to work just to keep things going.'

Brenda admitted that when she first went into the fields she thought that 'if you earned five shillings you'd gone to heaven', but she soon lost such optimistic attitudes.

Women and girls were frequently employed in dairy work, both as full-time workers and as casual – often unpaid – labour. June Good, later June Curtis, and her sisters had to take it in turns to clean the milk separator before school. 'It was a beautiful piece of machinery, but it had so many different parts,' she remembered.

As a member of a farmer's family, it would be automatically assumed that one would took a share of the work on the farm. Michael Read's first 'job' as a child was to try to catch the mice that came out of the stacks during threshing: 'We tried to drive them out so the dogs could catch them at the bottom.'

Even those who were not yet family were expected to put in their share of the work. Mandy Wyatt, on an early visit to the farm on which she now lives, was put to work on a combine:

'John [husband-to-be] showed me how to steer it and told me just to keep going round until it was finished, so I did that, but I didn't know what to do next. I didn't know where the next field was, and he hadn't shown me how to stop the combine, so I just carried on driving round and round, until I thought I ought to go and try to find the next field. I headed for the gate, which had a big tree alongside it. I had forgotten about the big pipe sticking out the side, but fortunately John came back just in time to stop me knocking it off on the tree, which was, of course, the only tree anywhere in the vicinity!'

The assumption that families were a useful source of unpaid labour continued, in my experience, well into the 1960s, when I left the family farm in large part to avoid such responsibilities. My brother, who returned to the farm, would doubtless argue that it went on for a lot longer than that!

Schoolchildren in Lincolnshire were expected to play a full part in many of the farm jobs. The autumn half-term holiday was set to allow them to help with the potato picking, and schoolboys like John Redhead could get a 'blue card' which allowed them to be off school when needed on the farm: 'From the age of eleven I put in many hours on blue card work – mostly horse-hoeing in those early days.'

■ *Effie and Cedric Wield helping with haymaking at Woodhall Spa. Under that pile of hay can probably be found the basket-work wheelchair which their father, John Wield, used to convey passengers from the railway station to the spa baths. The donkey pulled the chair then, as well.* (John Wield, courtesy of Woodhall Spa Cottage Museum.) ■

■ *Tea break for the Leggate family and staff at George Leggate's Manor Farm,*
Blankney Dales, in 1959: (l. to r.) Harry Diggins, George Leggate, Eddie Diggins,
Sam Leggate, Dave Lincoln, Bernard Leggate. (Sam Leggate) ■

GANGS GONE

ACHARACTERISTIC OF LINCOLNSHIRE FARMING used to be the presence of large gangs of workers at particular times of the year. Potato planting and lifting; flower, bulb and vegetable picking; sugar beet gapping, singling and lifting; grain harvest; and,

■ *Potato picking at Home Farm, West Pinchbeck, 1938.* (Reg Dobbs) ■

■ *Traditional gender roles in the potato field: six women planting, while three men drive the tractors!* (Author collection) ■

■ *A potato picking gang pause for a picture on a south Lincolnshire farm in the 1920s. The horse-drawn spinner is on the left of the picture, and the waggon is loaded with barrels into which the potatoes would be tipped from the baskets carried by the men.* (From the Museum of Lincolnshire Life, courtesy of Lincolnshire County Council.) ■

in the days before combines, threshing time, were all occasions when the regular farm labour force would be supplemented either by 'gangs' of Irish workers or female and casual labour from the local villages. Hoeing to control weeds, rogueing – walking through a grain crop and pulling wild oats or other problem weeds – and 'beating' to put up birds for the guns during a shoot could also involve significant numbers of extra hands, although these would normally be recruited locally for a few days at most.

The village workers would have lived at home, and either walked or cycled to work or got picked up by a farm or gangmaster's

■ *The snows of 1947 did not stop the potato riddling on Quincey's farm on the Witham Fens:* (l. to r.) *Mr Salmon senior, Tom Quincey, Peter Jackson, George Salmon, George Quincey, Fred Ingall.* (Sam Leggate) ■

wagon or lorry. Irish gangs were housed in so-called Paddy Houses, usually a disused cottage or farm building, although purpose-built accommodation or ex-military Nissen huts were sometimes made available. George Read housed his Irishmen in 'an old white cottage' on his farm, which was their base, although 'they all went to church at the weekend'. The men were supplied with firewood and potatoes in addition to their payment. The potatoes alone would not keep a man

fit for long spells of hard physical work, but they were supplemented with plenty of meat, either bought in or caught in the fields, with fat bacon being as important a part of their diet as it was to the regular farm hands. Vegetables, despite their relatively easy availability on many farms, didn't seem to be popular with the Irish.

Reg Dobbs, writing about the immediate post-war years, described the Paddy House at the farm next door as 'a purpose-built structure of brick or timber and corrugated iron'. The wife of the farm's foreman 'earned a shilling or two' by cooking meat, eggs and potatoes, as well as fetching bread and other necessities. She also cooked an evening meal for the gang, consisting of 'buckets of potatoes and pans of meat', which also provided the filling for the following day's sandwiches. On that farm, bunks were provided for the men, but others slept on sacks of straw or chaff, which were burnt after they left, with some comments that clearing the buildings after them was a job that the regular hands complained about. 'They stank, and the bags were often lousy,' one Sleaford hand commented. 'We'd get the women to do it if we could,

but they often seemed to be busy at the time!'

The Irish gangs worked hard – 'from dawn to dusk', according to Brian Waite, who claimed that they never wanted to go to bed – 'it was work or the pub, nothing else'. John Redhead had to join a gang when they were short of a complete team:

'There were four Irish and me and one other from the farm. The way they worked the first three days nearly killed me, but I learned from them, because that was the best way to keep your earnings up – the more you did, and the faster you did it, the more you earned.'

■ *Threshing with a drum at Nocton in the 1950s. A full threshing gang of at least ten men at work on the machines, the stacks and the bags.* (Len Woodhead) ■

■ *Irish workers forking vining peas into Parker Dean Produce's static pea viners situated on Metheringham Heath.*
The pea vine had been brought in from the fields on lorries. (Stuart Hemington) ■

Sam Leggate agreed that working with the Irish was hard, but profitable:

'After the war there were five of them – a father and his four sons, and if you could keep up with them you did very nicely out of it. They went from the potato picking here down to London, where they worked on building sites until Christmas, after which they went back home to the west coast of Ireland and took up their home trade of fishing.'

The gang Brian worked with had a similar routine, but they went to Leicester to work in the boot and shoe trade when not on the farm or at home.

Bob Fletcher also did well out of piece-work rates, until his father put a stop to it: 'Dad had us on piece work with a gang, but he thought it was costing him too much, so he put us on a salary!'

'Village' gangs were usually drawn from close at hand. I have a bunch of time sheets for the week ending 13 August 1955 for people potato picking on the farm of W. H. Willows of Tattershall. In that week, Derek and Terry Ranshaw, Dick Smith, Derick Pacey, Mrs G. Wells, Roland Lee, Tony Wells, David Pawley, Richard Wilson, G. Rouse, V. M. Ranshaw, W. Featherstone and John Speakman were all employed either on picking, loading or, in the case of Derek Ranshaw, burning potato tops at night. Mrs G. Speakman was weeding beet that week and Mr Featherstone dipped some sheep, as well as picking potatoes. All appear to have been on hourly rates, but these varied from 6½d (about 3 pence) for what appear from the handwriting to be children, through 1/6d to a top rate of £1.15s a day. There may well have been others, since the numbers on the sheets go up to 22, but all the workers shown came from the villages of Tattershall and Coningsby, both within a couple of miles of the farm.

Mary Sleaford, in the same area, pointed out that financial considerations were the main reason for working, but that there was a social side as well:

'With the twins and Eamonn at school we needed the money, but it was always good to be working with people you knew – we were

■ A gang of women taking a break from hoeing wheat on Holland Fen in 1947. (top row, l. to r.) Pem, Olive, Bertha; (middle), Doreen, Mary, Rachel, (bottom) Mrs Rumbelow, Denise and Margaret. (Mary Sleaford) ■

■ *A modern vegetable picking gang on Poplars Farm, near Holbeach Bank. The Polish team were cutting cauliflowers and field processing the curds into florets ready for freezing. The crop was grown by Lincolnshire Field Products.* (Gary Naylor) ■

never short of news about what was going on in the villages!'

Brenda Waite worked with a local gang of women from the villages of Benington and Leverton, near Boston:

'It was all local. The boss – we'd call him a gang master now – came from one of the villages, and we really only did four jobs: potato planting and picking, beet singling and taking cabbage plants out of the boxes in which they had been grown in greenhouses and bundling them ready for sending off to farmers for planting.'

The Irish had a reputation for working hard, but Mark Ireland found that the women were just as capable of setting a good pace:

'I got into trouble one year because I thought that if I just popped a few less potatoes into the bag, I could keep up with the women, but when they came to weigh the bags at the end, mine were too light, and they had to check them all before they went onto the lorry.'

Mark's father, Tony, was not a keen potato grower, but in the year of the great drought, 1976, he was pleased to be growing even a small area: 'Our 30 acres of potatoes gave a better return that year than 900 of barley.'

For a while the gangs were recruited from industrial towns in the Midlands, but Brenda Waite commented that they weren't always prepared for the work:

'One group of townies came onto the farm for the potato picking, and they wanted to know where the trees were from which they had to be picked. Their backs soon told them that they weren't picking from anywhere up in the air!'

Gang labour gradually faded away on most of the conventional arable farms in Lincolnshire by the 1970s, although Charles Ireland, Tony's uncle, continued with a spinner or hoover and pickers up to 1988. It has, however, remained an important part of the economy of the flower and vegetable growers in the south of the county right up to the present day. The workers nowadays tend to come from Eastern Europe or Portugal, with a sprinkling from the Middle and Far East.

The ending of the need for gangs and/or family labour also saw big changes in the villages. John Redhead moved to the village of Blyborough in 1951, and has seen the difference, 'When I went there, everyone in the village worked on the Blyborough estate, now there is just one who does.'

■ *A gang hoeing a well-established beet crop at Nocton.* (Len Woodhead) ■

THE END OF STEAM

S TEAM POWERED MANY farming operations from the middle of the 18th century, and it remained in use until after the Second World War, although the number of jobs had declined before that time. The use of traction engines to pull loads on the roads was one of the first tasks to go, as lorries became available after the First World War, although bigger loads, such as large timbers, continued to need the greater weight and pulling power of steam for some years. However, steam ploughing and threshing continued to be popular options.

Steam ploughing was considered to be essential on much of

■ *A steam ploughing set on the move near Croft in 1920. The lead engine is towing a plough and a cultivator, while the second is hauling the living van. The wheels of what is probably the water bowser can also be seen behind the van.* (From the Museum of Lincolnshire Life, courtesy of Lincolnshire County Council.) ■

■ *Threshing at Measure's Yard, Hacconby Lane, Morton, near Bourne, in 1921, with a Garratt portable engine. Bill Deacon is the driver; Albert 'Guffy' Ashton, the water boy; Bill Bayley; and George Taylor, in the checked jacket, can also be seen. The bike on which the driver would have ridden from home to get the engine in steam for the start of the day is in the left foreground.* (From the Museum of Lincolnshire Life, courtesy of Lincolnshire County Council.) ■

Lincolnshire's heavier land until crawlers began to take over in the 1930s. Early attempts to build steam machines that could work the fields themselves proved unsuccessful in British conditions since their weight caused them to sink into anything but the driest land. They were used in the USA and some British-built machines were sold to the Dominions. Three or six furrow ploughs or large multi-tined cultivators, hauled by cables to and fro across the field were the usual Lincolnshire tools. The implements were pulled either by two engines fitted with large cable drums under the boiler, or a single engine pulling against an anchor carriage on the opposite side of the field, although this was considered a less suitable option.

The ploughs were of the balanced type, with two sets of shares built like a see-saw. One set operated as the plough passed in one direction across the field, then the other set was rocked down into position to work as the implement went back towards the other side, ploughing equally well on both passes. Cultivators were single-direction tools, and had to be turned at the end of each pass. Steam power could also be used to dredge pond or drains, or create mole drains under the soil.

The steam ploughing gang usually consisted of five men: a foreman, two engine drivers, a ploughman and a cook, although there would sometimes be a lad to help with any odd jobs. They travelled with a set of two engines; one or two ploughs or a cultivator; a water cart; and a living van in which they all slept. Men and horses were supplied by the farm to keep the team supplied with coal and water, which had to be pumped up from ponds, streams or ditches using a pump incorporated into the water cart. The ploughing team were often on bonus rates, and any farm hand who failed to keep the supply of either commodity up to speed would be very unpopular. A particular problem was that

of horses refusing to go near the noisy engines. This meant that they had to be moved to the water cart, with a loss of time and wasted effort unhitching the plough or cultivator.

Ironically, present-day contractor Andrew Baxter counts the final days of the steam engines among his earliest memories:

'There was a big steam contracting company in Sleaford called Ward and Dale, and one of my earliest memories, was going with my dad and a big crawler tractor to help drag some of the old steam engines out when they had to clear their yard. They couldn't drive themselves by then so the only thing big enough to drag them was that crawler. That would probably have been in the late 1960s.'

■ *Buyers came from miles around for what is believed to be the dispersal sale of Ernest Harwood's steam engines and other equipment in the early 1940s. Mr Harwood was a contractor based at Spalding Common.* (Brian Lawrance) ■

■ *George Quincey and his Foster threshing drum at his farm sale in 1990.*
George had not used the drum for some years, but it was still in good condition.
(Sam Leggate) ■

Steam ploughing engines would also be put to work dredging lakes and big drains, but the other main use for steam on the farm was for threshing. A steam threshing set consisted of the engine, a threshing drum and an elevator or jackstraw, often abbreviated to 'jacker' on the farm, although a chaff cutter might also be included, along with a water bowser; again, though, coal and water were normally supplied by the farmer. A static baler might also be brought in if the farmer wanted the straw baled rather than stacked. The large majority of such sets were owned by specialist contractors, although the largest farms might own their own, and some owned a set in partnership with a contractor.

Up to a dozen men and boys would be employed during threshing, with the driver and his mate paid by the contractor, two or three others working for him on a fairly regular basis during the threshing season and the rest supplied by the farmer himself.

The key job in the team was the man who stood on top of the drum feeding the cut sheaves into the mechanism. If he got it too slow, the job took too long and wasted fuel, but too fast a feed could clog the drum or leave too much grain still attached to the ear. He was supplied with his material by someone, often a boy, who cut the strings on the sheaves and passed them to him on a 'just-in-time' basis – modern time and motion experts would have been impressed by the efficiency of the system!

George Curtis was one of the boys put to work cutting the bands, and he remembered that the man in charge of feeding the freed stalks into the drum would always check that the boy's feet were well secured in sheaves or other material before starting work. George was also taught to always cut the string close to the knot, leaving a useful length that could be used for tying sack necks or for other purposes round the farm. A bundle of slightly dusty lengths of string was, and often still is, characteristic of many farm buildings, although the string now comes from bales rather than sheaves.

Other jobs included passing the stacks of sheaves down to the drums, and moving the straw onto the stacks or into the baler. Reg Dobbs described those as favourite jobs because they were relatively clean. Least desirable was the task of working in the chaff hole or pult hole, where all the dusty rubbish came out and had to be bagged up and carted away. Reg also commented that few people found the extra rate of tuppence an hour attractive enough to make them volunteer to carry the 18-stone bags of grain from the drum up a ladder onto the wagon or into the granary above the barn.

Threshing machines continued to be used well after combines had become the main way of harvesting grain. Some seed merchants preferred machine-threshed grain, believing that combines reduced the quality of the seed, while some farmers found that the straw from a combine was not as good for covering the potato pies – earth and straw-covered in-field potato stores – as that from a threshing machine.

'We had two combines – a towed Minneapolis Moline tanker and a self-propelled Massey, but we only combined the barley at first, and put the wheat through the threshing machine, because that left the straw in bats to cover the potato pies.' [John Redhead]

■ *Steam traction engines were still the motive power of choice when hauling large loads. Harry Corps & Sons engines are moving a felled elm tree at Stainfield, reported to have been the largest in the county – a job that would have needed whole teams of horses.*
(Brian Lawrance) ■

In their later years, threshing machines were often driven by a tractor, rather than a steam engine. Marshalls of Gainsborough, who had specialised in threshing engines, developed a range of tractors culminating in the Field Marshall series, which were particularly well suited to driving a threshing set. Substituting a tractor for the engine did not affect other aspects of the job, although they were slightly less likely to set fire to the chaff or straw!

■ *Steam threshing on Ruskington Fen in the 1960s. The engine is* Evedon Lad, *and the water tank had probably seen service with the Forces a couple of decades earlier.* (From the Local Studies Collection, Lincoln Central Library, courtesy of Lincolnshire County Council.) ■

■ *A new threshing set being trialled on Mr Good's farm at Fiskerton. Mr Good can be seen standing on the threshing drum. The engine has been identified as a Ruston RLB, one of a batch built for export to the Baltic States. The final two machines were despatched in June 1935, and were the last traction engines to leave the Ruston works in Lincoln.* (June Curtis) ■

STEEL WHEELS TO POTATO FIELDS

∎

RAILWAYS PLAYED A KEY PART in the development of the potato industry in Lincolnshire since large amounts of the crop could now be transported quickly and easily from the county to the rapidly growing industrial cities of the North and Midlands. They also had a role to play on some of the farms themselves. Light railways, usually on ex-First World War narrow gauge 'Jubilee' track, were used on many of the large potato growing farms to help move the crates of seed potatoes into the fields and to carry the crop from the in-field storage clamps to a road or rail-head for movement off the farms. Stuart Squires, in his very comprehensive survey of the subject, has discovered about 50 such lines in the county. Similar tracks were also used by bulb growers in the south of the county, but their systems were not usually as extensive as those on the potato lands.

Most of the lines were on the flat lands of the Fens or the Isle of Axholme, where the rails could be easily laid and large loads moved by a horse or, in some of the more elaborate systems, by steam or internal combustion locomotives. The alternative, moving heavy loads on boggy cart tracks, using horses or even the early tractors, meant shifting smaller quantities at a time, using more men, much more slowly.

Some of the systems could be quite sophisticated. One of the earliest, started in 1909 on Wraggmarsh Farm, near Weston, included its own wharf on the River Welland, with a crane to load produce onto and off barges. The farmer, Mr George Caudwell, even had his own integrated transport system, eventually including his own tug and barges. The railway was originally operated by horse power, although gravity was

∎ *Unloading potatoes from the Fleet Light Railway at Fleet station. The light railway siding is at a higher level than that of the main line to make it easier to transfer the bags between the wagons.* (Tony Worth) ∎

■ *A shooting party about to depart on the Fleet Light Railway, near Holbeach. The host farmer, Mr A. H. Worth, is standing in the right foreground with a pipe and a dog.* (Tony Worth) ■

■ *Cleaning out the pig sties into the railway wagons at Town End Dunston on Smith's Potato Estate in 1960. (From the Museum of Lincolnshire Life, courtesy of Lincolnshire County Council.)* ■

extending into the farm's yards and buildings, eventually running up onto the higher lands of the Lincolnshire Heath to the west. It linked with the national railways system at an exchange siding at the local station.

The tracks were used for many other purposes than just carrying produce. Wagon loads of animal feed would be distributed to all the stockyards around the farms; fuel for the farm tractors was distributed by a weekly tanker train – each tractor had its own fuel bowser that was filled from the train; and drinking water for the 24 houses and cottages on the Fen, which had no mains supply, was distributed by rail, as was water for the stock if the conditions were too dry to pump water for them from the drains. The system even ran into the pig sties to make loading them with muck easier for the men.

The trains carried children to school in bad weather, collected and returned them for the annual sports day and even helped workers move house. Len Woodhead was moved from a cottage at Toddies Farm, on Nocton Fen to Foxes Farm when his father was made foreman, a job which came with a better house. The family's two pigs were sent ahead on a horse and cart, but everything else went by rail:

'An engine was sent with two box vans and two flat wagons, and with the help of some of the other men we loaded all our furniture and everything else into one or other of the wagons. The chickens had to be penned into one end of a box van with some wire fencing, but there was still enough room in one of them for us to sit in the armchairs, with the door open, and enjoy the view as we travelled along.'

In addition to the fixed lines, Len remembered that new sidings would be installed very quickly where needed.

'When we were lifting beet, the platelayers would be down on the previous night with a wagon carrying two or three panels of track. They would lay those in the next field to be lifted, and wagons brought down to be filled. We used horses and carts to move the beet to the wagons, and they were then taken away by the engines. Up to six wagons could be moved at one time, and they would be

used to take loaded wagons down from the main farm to the wharf. A locomotive powered by a tractor engine provided the motive power in later years.

The Fleet Light Railway, owned by the Worth family, included just over twelve miles of track, although that extended to nearly twenty miles if you include the neighbouring system built on Thomson's Farms at Dawsmere, which had an end-on connection to the Fleet lines. Like most of the Lincolnshire potato railways, these lines crossed public roads at several points, including the main A17, a situation that would create chaos nowadays on a highway that carries huge volumes of produce and other merchandise between Lincolnshire and East Anglia.

The largest system, on the Nocton estate owned by Smith's Potato Chips, ran for over 20 miles, mostly on the Witham Fens, but also

61

taken down to the river, where there was a weighbridge that would check the weight before the beet was carried on the gantry to the sugar factory on the other side.'

Some of the railways also served a leisure purpose, with trains used to transport shooting parties out onto the land. Nocton owned a single passenger carriage which was used for this and other purposes, but the guns on the Fleet Light Railway had to be content with riding on open flat wagons, although the shot game did have a truck to itself.

■ *Wagons at the railhead by the main-line station on the Nocton estate. Produce could be transferred here for onward movement, or goods such as seed potatoes collected from the train for movement into the chitting houses. Tommy Asher is switching the points.* (Len Woodhead) ■

OLD FRIENDS

◆

THE USE OF HORSES ON THE FARM declined after the First World War, being gradually replaced by the tractor on the farm and the lorry off it, but the change didn't happen at the same rate in all parts of the county, and was regretted by many of the people involved. Working with horses was hard – the horseman usually walked beside or behind his charges and looking after them took up a substantial part of the working day, as well as some of the little time that he might have expected to spend at rest or with family or friends. When the tractor arrived the worker could ride, and the after-care was usually limited to some basic servicing and refuelling, but no ex-horseman that I ever spoke to wasn't sad when their animals went, although every one admitted that life was easier without all the walking, feeding and grooming.

'There was a partnership between the horses and the waggoner

■ *Two horse and waggon teams, with the loaders ready for a day in the hayfields; believed to be at Fiskerton c.1928.* (Roland Marshall) ■

■ *Bob Wilkinson not only worked his horses; he was proud to show them as well. He took many prizes at the Woodhall Show and other agricultural events.* (Dorothy Wilkinson)■

– he cared for them and they worked for him. It was much more than a man and a tractor, and something ended on the farm when the horses went.' [Terry Atkinson]

Those who had less direct involvement with the horses, like Bob Scarborough, did point out that the horses themselves might have welcomed the arrival of the tractor.

'I'm not one of those that moans about the tractors taking over from the horses. I really think that horses that worked on a farm had a hard life and a short life, so I think it has been a good thing overall.'

Virtually all the horsemen treated their animals as well as – and sometimes better than – their own families. The recipes for strange concoctions to cure, calm or enliven their charges were kept secret by their devisers, and were only passed on to other family members or close friends. Feed mixtures and timings were carefully controlled, although the amounts that the farmer considered to be appropriate for the horses were not always considered adequate by the horsemen. They were well known for their propensity to steal a little extra from the farm stores to keep their own stock in prime condition. Locking the grain store wasn't enough to stop them, since stories suggest that they made, or had made, copies of any keys to buildings on the farm. Others helped themselves from the threshing drum, and stored a bag or two of grain elsewhere on the farm, to be dipped into when needed. One man was even reported to have crawled under the floor of a granary, which had been raised off the ground to keep out rats and mice, and drilled a hole up through the floor into a full bag of grain. After filling a bucket he would block the hole again with a cork until he needed another top-up.

They knew the optimum rate for working – 'for the sake of the horses you need to be steady and regular,' I was told. Hurrying tired the horses more and slowed the work over the whole day. Getting the right team for the job was also important. Two horses were all that were needed for a single furrow plough or a simple reaper, but three were needed for two-furrow ploughing or to work a binder, with its

■ *Some of the last ploughing jobs undertaken by horses were to close the final furrow between strips of tractor ploughing or to plough out the headlands where the tractor had been turning. Jack Pick is seen here with the horses ploughing the headlands on a farm at Tattershall in 1952. His brother, Charles, standing (left), has just come down with the farm's Morris commercial lorry to help load the plough into the cart pulled by their International W4, driven by Tom Bemrose. The tractor is still owned by Charles' son, Richard.* (Richard Pick) ■

■ *In 1946 W.R. (Reg) Hargreaves from Gernsgate Hall Farm, Long Sutton, backed* Airborne *to win both the Derby and the St Leger. With his winnings he bought a shire colt which he named* Airborne *as well. Reg (on horse) and his son John (leading), seen here in 1952, continued to use* Airborne *on the farm through to the 1960s, when it was the last horse on the farm, skerrying strawberries, carting muck and taking beet to the local station. John's son, Alan, followed the family tradition in later years by backing* Motivator *to win the 2005 Derby and naming his Lincoln Red bull* Walmer Motivator *after him.* (Alan Hargreaves) ■

additional mechanisms and increased weight. Grass cutting could be done with one horse and a three-foot cut, but it was generally agreed that one horse couldn't cut going uphill, so single-horse hay cutting could be a tedious job on the Wolds.

Geoff Robinson might have disagreed with the tedious description: on one occasion, while working on a farm at Sutton on Sea he found the whole thing a bit too exciting.

'I was working down the side of a long field, with a grass reaper behind a pair of horses when a Meteor jet and a Vampire came over. The horses weren't used to that and just took off sideways across the middle of the field. The boss wanted to know what on earth we were doing with one cut straight across! It was a nuisance to me as well, because I had to lift the bed of the reaper every time we went across that sideways cut.'

The horsemen needed to know their own land. One man who had been brought up on the Wolds was offered more money to come and work on the heavier soils of the Witham Fens, but he gave up after a few weeks because he couldn't get used to the slower pace and the unfamiliar setting.

A special category among the horsemen was the men who travelled stallions – took them round other farms to 'cover' the mares. My grandfather, Alex Young, was one of them, although I find it hard to imagine that rather dour Scotsman sitting in his parlour with the paper as someone sharing the rather raffish reputation enjoyed by some of his fellows! He was a known local authority on horses, and, as his daughter

■ *Fred Nixon showing one of Arthur Leggate's carts at the Woodhall Spa Show in 1950. The horse is decorated with brasses for the show.* (John Harrison) ■

Eileen, my mother, recalled in her memoirs,

'When the vet from the adjoining village had a call about horses, it was said he always asked, "Have you seen Alex Young? He'll put you right!" Many a time he has got up from his Sunday dinner in order to see some new foal or help out, and Sunday dinners were pretty sacrosanct in our family.'

He first travelled with stallions owned by local farmers, but his great aim was to have 'entires' – stallions – of his own, which he managed by the middle 1930s. Unfortunately, Eileen remembered, 'He couldn't have chosen a worse time, as tractors were taking the place of horses, and the farmers who did need his services were generally too hard up to pay their bills!'

The pride in their animals often extended well beyond the farm and into the local show-rings. Heavy Horse classes and horse-drawn turnouts were important elements in most agricultural shows well into

the 1960s, and they remain a popular attraction to this day, although most of the horses rarely need to pull a plough. The beautifully-decorated carts and waggons are now the realm of enthusiastic preservationists who would turn pale at the sight of their cart being loaded with fresh muck or the waggon hauled across a muddy field.

The availability of smaller tractors was often a key element in the final changeover from horses. When Michael Lambert took over a farm at Donington from his father in the 1950s he soon made the switch: 'Father wasn't very keen on machinery, so we had fourteen horses at that time, but as soon as I got the reins they quickly went and Fergusons replaced them.' On the Nocton estates bigger steel-wheeled tractors had been in use before the war, but better roads and rubber tyres saw Fordsons and Fergusons replace the horses. For each rubber-tyred tractor that was purchased, four horses left the farm.

■ *Prospective buyers inspecting horse-drawn implements at Stainfield, near Bourne, in 1969, after Frank Measures replaced his horses with a contractor.* (David Creasey) ■

■ *The wagon repair shop at Nocton, still dealing with cart wheels in the 1960s. Mr Hemmings and his son Fred.* (Len Woodhead) ■

■ *A horse-drawn seed drill, the first product made by Ken Tong, who founded what is now vegetable and potato handling specialists Tong Peal Engineering, based at Spilsby.* (Edward Tong)■

On a smaller farm out near the coast, Geoff Robinson had been using horses in the early 1950s for grass cutting, raking and harrowing in the summer, and for kale carting in the winter. The purchase of a 'little grey Fergie', however, to do the same jobs by the farmer saw the end of his working horse days. 'They did have a Case petrol/paraffin tractor that did all the ploughing before that, but it wasn't used for the lighter jobs – that was where Duke and Bonnie had been used, but the Ferguson took over all those jobs.' The same happened on my father's farm, with another Fergie taking on the haulage jobs.

Despite the apparent advantages, the changeover from horses to tractors was gradual. Many farmers could not afford the capital investment needed to buy the new machines, particularly since the horse had the useful attribute that it could renew itself as a power source by giving birth to a foal. A tractor also suffered from the inability to answer to a spoken command; not just a problem when it refused to stop when told, but also because someone had to keep jumping on and off the seat when a cart needed moving a few feet up a field. A shout would bring a horse-drawn cart up to the next pile of beet, or a waggon alongside a stook of sheaves. In fact, the shout was sometimes not needed, since an experienced horse would often move up of its own accord, keeping abreast of the team of men. Horses were often used alongside the tractors, doing lighter work such as harrowing or rolling behind a tractor that was ploughing or deep cultivating.

'In 1953 we used a horse to load hay in the field, but we didn't use a full harness or put it into shafts. We just used the ploughing chains and hitched them to the towbar on the waggon with a hook. That way we had the benefit of the horse moving when it was told, but we could bring a tractor in to take the load back to the yard. It meant the horse waited in the field till the waggon came back, but it was still faster than using the horse all the time.' [Geoff Robinson]

Geoff did return to the horses later, when he became a well-known Shire breeder on a small farm at Metheringham.

'I got a job as a rep in 1961, and I bought 30 acres of grass and kept beef cattle on it. I'd always wanted to be a farmer and I loved the horses, so in '67 I bought my first Shire. It was a good one to buy, since it was the best example of a bad horse that I ever saw – I learned more from that animal than from any other that I have ever owned!'

According to Geoff, the last working horses that he could remember in the county were at a farm in Ruskington in 1970: 'Ted Phillips was still using them for potato carting – an Irish gang picked and the horses carted.'

Carting was often the final job that horses had on farms. Alan Hargreaves remembered carting beet to the railway station at Long Sutton to load it into wagons for transport to the factory.

'Dad also used a horse for skerrying strawberries – the horse stepped between the rows, and the little single wheel followed while dad steered the three duck-foot tines with the handles to take out the weeds.'

Horses were not the only animals to be departing from Lincolnshire farms. Many farmers simply gave up livestock altogether and concentrated on arable, but those who kept stock usually modernised the breeds and the systems.

The cottager's pig gradually disappeared, although I was present at an unofficial back garden pig killing as late as the 1980s, but our own Lincolnshire Curly-coat faded out a decade earlier. It was too fat for more modern tastes, and was first replaced by breeds like the Essex and Berkshire, or was crossed with leaner breeds to improve the offspring.

'I kept Lincolnshire Curly-coated pigs as a boy, but they were always put to a Landrace boar to get a less fat carcase.' [Brian Pickwell]

Pigs had also generally moved out of the individual sty and into open yards. Jack Waite worked with Large Black/Large White cross pigs that were kept in the same yards as the cattle.

■ *Taking coals to Newcastle? According to legend, the Durham Ox was one of the founding animals of the Lincoln Red breed, so it might seem presumptuous to be holding a Lincoln Red sale in Durham in 1950.* (David Harrison) ■

'They had their own corner where they were fed, but they mixed in with the stock in the yards, picking up anything that they dropped to the ground. They had to stop that when the TB testing came in, but they had nowhere else to put them, so they had to go.'
[Brian Waite]

Pigs are now largely to be found in specialised units, either housed in large open buildings or kept outdoors with basic shelters to shield them from the worst of the weather. The same has happened to poultry, although the different systems vary considerably, from intensive caged birds to free-range units which allow a considerable degree of outdoor space. Most, though, are still kept in large units rather than roaming the farmyard picking up whatever they can find, and laying just for the benefit of the farmer and his family, as would have been the case on most farms a few decades ago.

As the demand for the long staple wool from our local Lincoln Longwool sheep breed declined, so did its numbers in the county, along with the system of keeping the sheep on drier land in the winter, and taking them to better pastures through the summer. The Suffolk breed, still the most popular native breed in the UK, found Lincolnshire land very similar to that of its native county. For those not keeping pedigree stock, a more common option was to bring in North Country Mules

■ *Mr John Marvin milking a shorthorn cow by hand on his smallholding in Morton.* (Brian Lawrance) ■

– a cross of northern hill sheep with a more commercial ram – and to cross those again with Suffolks to produce a finished carcase. In more recent years, continental breeds such as Texel, Charollais and Beltex have become more important. In so far as Lincolnshire still has a sheep sector, the 'flying flocks' which feed on vegetable crops waste are an important part.

Our local Lincoln Red cattle breed is still with us, with a thriving market sector in quality beef, but nobody now wins prizes for milking ability, as happened in the 1920s, and its role as the principal beef animal in the county has been largely taken over by the continental breeds that have come into the county in the past 40 years or so.

Dairy farmers also milked breeds such as brown and white Ayrshires and the red, white or red roan Dairy shorthorns. Brian Baines worked with a herd of Ayrshires when he first left school in the 1950s:

'I had my favourites, but they were mostly very docile, although there were always one or two who knew just when to aim a kick at you – usually just as you went to put the cluster on.'

These traditional dairy breeds all had the benefit, as seen at the time, of producing good, creamy milk. Despite that, Dickie Hill, as a land girl during the war, milked a herd that felt it needed to boost the cream content: 'We were milking a hundred Ayrshires, but the owners still had three Guernseys to improve the butterfat.'

■ *An unusual sight for Lincolnshire: a herd of Belted Galloway cattle in the park by Northorpe Hall, near Gainsborough.* (Robert Dickinson) ■

The black and white Friesians that were replacing them produced a thinner milk, considered less desirable by most farmers. Kevin Willoughby's father was one of the first to introduce Friesians into the Lincolnshire Marsh.

'He went into dairy in 1956, by buying three of the newcomers from the market in Lincoln – he had wanted four, but they were too expensive, so he bought three and 200 chickens – the eggs eventually paid for the fourth cow. When he got back, all his neighbours, who kept Ayrshire cows, told him that the Friesians would be useful at the end of the parlour, where the "warm water" they produced would be good for washing up the equipment!'

Kevin had the last laugh – nearly half his current herd is descended from one of those first three cows.

The view that dairy farmers could be old-fashioned might have got some support for another incident remembered by Dickie: 'We girls were never allowed to be on the spot when cows were being served by the bull – the manager thought that wouldn't have been nice!'

■ *The author's grandfather and father, Herbert and Norman Stennett, with a prize-winning Shorthorn in 1935.* (Author's collection) ■

■ *The move to black and white Friesian dairy cattle was well under way by the late 1960s. The author's father had moved towards them from a miscellaneous collection of types, and his grand-daughter Marian took a close interest in the newest arrivals.* (Author) ■

■ *Her Majesty The Queen at the presentation of the Burke Trophy for the best pair of a breed at the Royal Show in 1972.* (Left to right*) Brian Waite with the bull* Frithville Kingpin, *from the herd of Coupland Bros; Lincoln Red breeder Mr C. L. (Lol) Bembridge and judge Tom McTurk.* (Brian Waite) ■

Horseless Horse-power

Tractors started to come into Lincolnshire before the First World War, but they only really took off after that conflict as more practical machines began to become available. The first ones were relatively low-powered, somewhat unreliable and needed new skills on the part of farm workers and mechanics.

If we leave aside the attempts to build steam tractors capable of working directly in the fields, or such monsters as the Marshall oil engines, which were basically a steam engine chassis with a large oil engine mounted on top, the first British-made tractor as we would recognise it today was the Ivel, built by Dan Albone in Bedfordshire. It appeared at the Royal Show in 1903, but the death of Albone in 1906 slowed development, and it failed to make a significant mark on the

■ *Sadly, not a good picture, but one of a unique machine. This tractor was built by Henry Burtt for use on his Hall Farm at Dowsby. It was assembled by Foleys of Bourne based on a redundant steam engine and a car, using a Napier engine.*
(Brian Lawrance) ■

■ An unidentified driver with a small Cletrac crawler tractor, of the type that took part in the Lincoln tractor trials of 1919.
(John Wield, courtesy Woodhall Spa Cottage Museum.) ■

market. Saunderson, also of Bedford, introduced a number of models before and during the First World War, and were, for some time, Britain's largest manufacturer of tractors. Unfortunately, none of the early British manufacturers could produce in large enough numbers to meet the demand for increased food production during that war. Henry Ford in the USA was therefore approached by the UK government, and commissioned to supply the country with 7,000 of his Fordson Model F, the world's first mass-produced tractor, known here originally as the MOM – Ministry of Munitions – tractor. As a current owner of a Model F, Laurie Nicholson, pointed out: 'It was cheap, you could mend

it with a hammer and it pulled well – and still does! What more could you want?'

Selling at £130, it dominated the market, but that did not prevent other, locally-produced, machines from making a bid for sales. In 1919 the British government organised a series of trials for tractors, held near Lincoln, at which 31 models were entered by more than two dozen companies, including six designed and built in Lincolnshire.

Blackstone, from Stamford, put in two machines, but the judges were concerned that they might be 'too complicated for the average farm hand'. Claytons, from Lincoln, entered a track-laying machine,

■ *A Saunderson tractor working with a binder on Dowsby Fen in 1925. Alf Biggadyke is driving the tractor, with Reg Wyles standing and A. Wyles on the binder.* (Brian Lawrance) ■

■ *YFC machinery training. A decoking demonstration by J. Vinter, NAAS (National Agricultural Advisory Service) at Trafford's farm, Scredington. (Chris Richardson)* ■

tended to catch fire, and the Fordson and Maskell tractors should not be used on sloping fields because of the absence of brakes!

John Deere was another overseas company offering tractors to the UK market during the First World War. Their Waterloo Boy model was actually designed by the Overtime Company, which was taken over by Deere, and some tractors sold here still carried that name. Derek Mellor owns a preserved example, but he says it was well up to the jobs required of it: 'It was a hard slogger, designed for pulling a two to three furrow plough. It was quite a reliable tractor. I've had no trouble with working it for thirty years – it just keeps going!'

A similar set of trials was held near Oxford in 1930, where some rather more familiar names, including five Caterpillar models, a Case, one from Massey Harris and Marshalls. Ironically, the most successful tractor of the years before and during the Second World War, the Fordson Model N, failed at the trials. It suffered a cracked engine block, and had to be withdrawn, although that didn't seem to affect its popularity then, or later, among tractor buyers.

The change from horses to tractors also saw a change in what might be described as vehicle maintenance. The horse itself needed a farrier, although the local blacksmith usually did that job, as well as any miscellaneous metal repairs or manufacture. Horse-drawn machinery was often built with a significant proportion of wood in its construction, so carpenters and wheelwrights were always required – either on the farm or in the immediate vicinity. Any iron and steelwork needed had to be dealt with by the local blacksmith unless it was something particularly intricate or specialised.

designed to haul a four-furrow plough, although the price of over £600 would have put off many prospective buyers. A few still survive in preservation, and Arthur Hinch has been involved with their restoration: 'For its day, it must have been a good tractor compared to what else they had available. They did thresh with them – I have a picture of one driving a threshing machine.'

All the machines in the trials had to have the drive pulley power checked, since providing power for threshing drums, saw-benches and other machinery would be an important job for the new machines.

In their overall conclusions, the judges stated that most of the machines were 'perfectly sound' although some were easier to work on than others. They also appended a note on safety, which stated that 'none of the machines could be considered in any way unsafe if handled with reasonable care' although they pointed out that the Pick entrant

Vintage combine restorer Ron Knight pointed out that the handbook for a 1920s American combine that he was working on specified every detail of its construction, from the type and size of wooden elements to the precise angle of bent iron work or the gauge of the steel tinwork: 'They worked on the assumption that anyone repairing it would not be a specialist, but would be able to do most things well providing they knew what to use.'

As the tractor took over, the first move was to modified horse implements, but with steel tow-bars replacing wooden shafts, then to bigger stronger tackle to stand up to the greater pulling power. A lot of the work could still be carried out on the farm, and farm workshops became more adept at dealing with the necessary repairs.

■ *Tinsley workshop. The need for greater mechanical sophistication on farms led to better equipped workshops, like this one on Tinsley's farms at Holbeach.* (H. Tinsley) ■

Organisations such as Young Farmers Clubs held training courses in the new technologies, but the more recent proliferation of electronic controls and systems has resulted in an increased need to refer to the local agent, or the original manufacturer.

'I used to be able to look inside the combine, and know what had gone wrong – now I look at all those black boxes, and I close the inspection panel and phone for help!' [Geoff Hotchkin]

The place he phoned to for help would be the local dealer, a trade that grew from a number of small beginnings. Robert Crawford was a blacksmith before taking on an International Harvester franchise that later developed into a knowledge of all things Marshall. Henry Peacock, who founded Peacock and Binnington, started out as a salesman for the Leeds Wagon Co, but diversified in partnership with a Mr Binnington, selling agricultural machinery, spares and panels of railway track to farmers needing easier access to wet potato fields. The company was already selling Massey Harris equipment when it moved to its present site in Brigg in 1904, and has maintained the link with its successor, Massey Ferguson, to the present day. R.W. Marsh in Sleaford began by running their own threshing engine sets, and moved on to become specialists in harvesting machinery.

'We did sell tractors, but we never settled on any of them. It used to be said that we represented every tractor company there was at one time or another except John Deere, but that wasn't our main business.' [Gordon Cumming]

Levertons of Spalding started in 1901 as a cycle shop, but an appointment as a government tractor representative during the Second World War took them into the business. Friskneys of Horncastle also started in a cycle shop. The original Mr Friskney built a shed alongside his house in Baumber in 1909, but moved the business to Horncastle in 1911. The company became Ford agents in 1917, and kept that franchise until after Ford tractors were merged into a bigger business in recent years. Friskneys are now the only agricultural machinery dealers in the town, but Managing Director, Eric Young, knew of many more in the past: 'There were Warrens, Snowdens, Achurch and several others, all of them getting their business from the farmers in and around the town.'

Local manufacturers also made the switch from horse-drawn implements to those more suitable to tractors. Shafts went, to be replaced by drawbars, and the availability of power takeoff from the tractor avoided the need to drive any mechanism from the road wheels.

A major development of the inter-war years was the introduction of the Ferguson System, a three-point linkage on the back of the tractor that allowed the development of many more tractor-mounted implements. The system also provided automatic depth control of a plough, by varying the back-pressure on the tractor exerted by the top link. As a valuable side-benefit, it effectively stopped the tractor when the plough hit an immovable object such as a large rock, a tree root, or, particularly relevant to the Lincolnshire fens, the semi-fossilised tree trunk known as a bog oak.

Most tractors of the inter-war years were either fuelled by petrol or a paraffin-based fuel known as tractor vaporising oil – TVO. TVO was the cheaper fuel, but starting a tractor on it was very difficult, so they were usually started on petrol and switched over to the main fuel when they were running well: 'You had to let the engine warm up before you let the paraffin in – when the smoke changed colour, you knew it was getting there.'

The need for a hotter engine meant that some TVO tractors had a moveable screen in front of the radiator for particularly cold conditions, or when the tractor was working for a long period under light loads.

Some diesel tractors, also known as oil-burners, were built during that period. Diesel engines had the advantage of being mechanically simpler, longer-lived and offering more flexible power due to their ability to pull better at lower revs. Marshalls, in particular, made use of their own single-cylinder diesel engine, which gave the tractors their characteristic 'popping' exhaust sound, but also covered the driver in a light film of oil droplets. They were also more difficult to start. Getting a Marshall to run involved placing a piece of glowing paper – or occasionally a cigarette end – in a holder in the cylinder. The tractor is then spun over several times in a decompressed state by a starting handle in the fly-wheel. When sufficient momentum has been built up, the engine is allowed to compress and, if you are skilful or lucky, it fires. An alternative was to insert a special cartridge into a location on the intakes, and hit it with a hammer. The explosion drives a charge into the engine, turning it over and, again, hopefully, it fires. Marshall drivers tended to have strong right arms. The very similar Lanz Bulldog also used a single-cylinder diesel engine, but this was started by heating a hot bulb under the engine with a blow-lamp.

■ *The original home and shop of John Thomas Friskney, the founder of J. T. Friskney, at Baumber.* (Eric and Gwen Young) ■

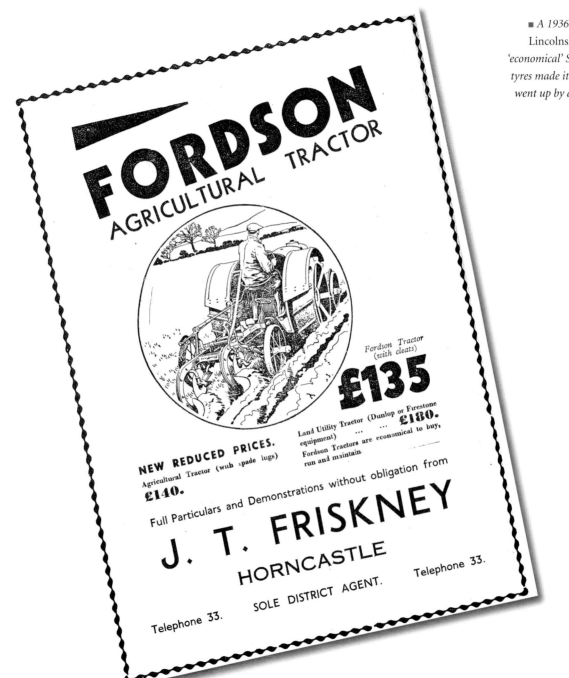

■ *An International Titan working near Woodhall Spa in the 1920s. The Titan was one of a number of American tractors brought over to Britain during or immediately after the First World War.*
(John Wield, courtesy Woodhall Spa Cottage Museum.) ■

'They would usually start up okay, although they did catch fire fairly easily, and it was quite possible to start the engine running backwards, which was rather a nuisance …'

Diesel engines for a wide range of tractors did not become popular until after the Second World War, when a combination of the availability of self-starters and a rise in the comparative price of petrol made them commercially and operationally attractive, as well as giving the power benefits already referred to. Perkins diesel engines were fitted to a variety of tractor makes, either as an original option, or as a conversion kit. Such machines were often marked by a Perkins badge on the radiator, and the frequency with which that badge is seen at

preservation events is a mark of the success of the modification.

Sometimes the decision not to buy a tractor was taken on more practical grounds. Marshalls delivered one of their new models to a farm at Pilham, near Gainsborough, in the 1930s. Unfortunately, the machine resolutely refused to start, despite the close attention of three of the company's own mechanics. When invited to complete the deal, the farmer, George Sleight, refused the offer, commenting, not unreasonably, that if the firm's own people couldn't get it to start, what chance did he have? Ironically, Mr Sleight had only recently bought the farm from Marshalls themselves.

Another Fordson – the Model N – became the dominant force

■ *Health and safety? Seven-year-old Tom Woods standing on the mudguard of an International 15/20 on Sam Frere's farm on Pinchbeck Fen, in about 1933. Jack Twell is driving the tractor with Tom's father Alf, on the binder. (Fanny Twell)* ■

in tractors on Lincolnshire farms before the Second World War and during the early years of the conflict. The Model N started the war in a distinctive orange livery, but the apparent ease with which they could be spotted in the fields and targeted by German fighters led to the adoption of a less visible green livery.

Tractors needed mechanical knowledge to keep them working, so horsemen often found it difficult to switch steeds, although one of George Read's waggoners made the move easily enough. George and his son Dick met him as he was coming onto the farm in 1947 after being away in the forces. The waggoner, also called George, told them that he was hoping for his job back, but the farmer said there was no work now for a waggoner. 'He asked him where he had been, and why it had taken him so long to get back,' Dick said, 'but when he said he'd been in Egypt driving Sherman tanks for the past five years, Father hired him immediately. If he can drive a tank, he said, he can certainly manage a tractor!'

The tractors that really made a difference on Lincolnshire farms were the American machines that came in during the Second World War and immediately afterwards under the Lend-Lease scheme.

Stephen James, from Barton on Humber, still has the John Deere BN that he used in his youth.

'My Dad was the foreman, and I drove it during harvest when I was off school during holidays. It was usually a field tractor – it had an underslung scuffler [a set of tines to cultivate or weed between rows] to scuffle sugar beet, but that was taken off during harvest so it could be used for leading sheaves to the stacks. It was brilliant to drive then, and it still is!'

John Deeres were popular tractors when I was a small child in South Lincolnshire, where they were sold by the local firm of Levertons in Spalding. As row-crop tractors, their tricycle wheel arrangement and underslung implements worked well in potato, beet and vegetable fields.

■ *A Land Army girl starting a Fordson tractor at Swineshead in the 1940s.* (From the Museum of Lincolnshire Life, courtesy of Lincolnshire County Council.) ■

TO GROW MORE FOOD.
Farm workers and members of the Women's Land Army receiving instruction on practical tractor work, organised by the Lindsey C.C.

■ *George Bradshaw, from machinery dealers Peacock and Binnington, in Brigg, training a Land Girl and others how to operate a standard Fordson tractor during the Second World War.* (Peacock and Binnington) ■

'It hoed sugar beet, hilled potatoes up, did a lot of weeding – the visibility of the implements was very good – you sat on the seat and everything was in front of you, although it wasn't good in dry conditions because you were sitting straight over the dust!' (JD Model A – Rodney Effield)

Terry Atkinson was impressed by the Massey tractor that he drove in the Sixties:

'It had loads of power. We had filled a lorry with sacks of potatoes, but it had sunk into its axles in the field. We had to get it out, and across another grass field, so we yocked it onto the middle hitch, which you weren't supposed to do and took it flat out. We dragged it across the grass, making great big ruts as it came, but that Massey did the job. I don't like to think, though, what would have happened if the lorry had hit something in the ground, because the tractor would have just turned straight over and landed on its back.'

Locally-built tractors became more available after the war. Fordson replaced their Model N first with the E27N Major, then a range of more stylish Majors and Super Majors. American firms such as International Harvester and Allis Chalmers manufactured or assembled tractors in the UK, but they met competition from Ferguson, Marshall, David Brown and Nuffield, among others. Pulling power and reliability were the first considerations of a prospective buyer, but comfort began to play a part. The old steel seat, padded with a bit of straw in a hessian sack, could be replaced by a more comfortable option. Brian Baines liked the Nuffield that he drove, but a more luxurious option was offered on the David Brown Cropmaster in the shape of a bench seat big enough for two. Quite who the other occupant was intended to be was never very clear, but one chap told me that he took a prospective girlfriend with him on one occasion. He didn't record whether he was able to keep the furrow straight, but he did remark that she never took him up on the offer again.

■ *A Series 3 Field Marshall at work near Gainsborough in about 1957.* (Roland Marshall) ■

MECHANICAL MARVELS
– GRASS AND GRAIN

Mechanisation of Lincolnshire farms had begun during the 19th century, with steam engines, threshing drums and horse-drawn reciprocating knife mowers to be found all over the county. During the 20th century a whole range of ingenious machines began to be employed to do work that had once needed many men or heavy tackle. Some of them worked well, but others were temperamental to say the least, and sometimes impossible to use in field conditions. Steam and threshing have been covered earlier, but the mower took on new forms over the next 100 years. Where grass-cutting, for hay and silage, was concerned, it first moved onto the back of tractors, with power take-off drives (PTOs) replacing the older wheel-driven system. The increased power meant that blockages were less frequent, although the fact that the blade no longer stopped automatically when the wheels stopped can lead to accidents when a blockage does have to be cleared.

'There was a little lever at the side of the seat that took it out of gear – there was an absolute rule that you didn't put your fingers anywhere near the bar to clear it until that was put into the safe position.' [Geoff Robinson's memory of health and safety rules in the 1950s!]

■ *David Gibson, far left, and his son Gerald, far right, trying out a second-hand binder they were thinking of buying for their farm. It was their first PTO driven binder, powered by the Fordson Major, being driven by Lesley Mason. Elise Carlton is waiting to stook the sheaves. (Brian Lawrance)* ■

■ *The old and the new in the harvest field. Colin Dickinson driving a 1922 Fordson Model F tractor, pulling his pre-1900 Massey Harris sail reaper, with Ken Renshaw on the seat on David Read's Barr Farm at Edlington. Following close behind is David Read's New Holland CX860 combine. The reaper is only taking a part breadth across the field – a full breadth of the modern high-yielding was too much for the reaper to handle! The tractor is also fitted with an underslung reaper, carried in a vertical travelling position. (Colin Dickinson)* ■

■ *Man, horse and tractor power together. Two binders, one pulled by a tractor, the other by three horses, at work in a field on Burnham Beeches Farm, near Thornton Curtis, in the 1930s. Mr James Fussey is riding on the first binder. Three men are also at work stooking the sheaves.* (R. Wood) ■

■ *Loading sheaves onto a waggon near Woodhall Spa. Getting down from the top of a load before it moved off to the yard could be a tricky operation.* (John Wield, courtesy Woodhall Spa Cottage Museum.) ■

Later competitors to the knife as the cutting tool included rotary mowers, in either drum or disc form, and flail mowers, which had the added advantage of helping condition the crop – bruise it to allow the moisture to leak out – which allowed it to dry more quickly. The drive was not always taken from the PTO. One early rotary machine took its power by way of a belt drive from the pulley on the tractor, transferred through another pair of pulleys on the front axle, resulting in a power train that looks positively dangerous to modern eyes. Another, the

Taarup Flying Saucer, caused unacceptable losses among the pheasants in the fields by slicing them in half as it passed over – by the time the birds realised it was a threat it was too late to get up and fly away. The farm on which Eamonn Sleaford was working devised its own pheasant protection system. 'We fitted a bar across the front of the tractor, with chains hanging down from it. I'm not sure if it was the noise or actually being hit that got them up, but they certainly stayed clear of the cutters'.

Hay rakes, sweeps, tedders and swath turners remained the province

■ *A Ford 4000 tractor pulling a wuffler on Bob Scarborough's farm at Skellingthorpe. The wufflers fluffed up the hay to help it dry more quickly.* (Bob Scarborough) ■

■ Fred Richardson on a Fordson tractor, with his brother 'Tim' on the binder at Grove Farm, Swaton, in the late 1920s/early 1930s.
(Chris Richardson) ■

of horse-haulage for some time, although sweeps and buck-rakes saw early attempts to mechanise them by attaching them to the front of motor cars. Eventually, though, most of them were hauled by, or mounted on the back of, tractors, to benefit from PTO power where needed. Mostly men working with pitchforks remained the way that loose hay was loaded in the field and taken to the stacks, but a variety of mechanical pick-up systems did come into use for larger farms.

The switch in the 1940s and 1950s from hay to silage was greatly assisted by new and modified machinery. It was quite possible to make it by cutting the grass with a grass reaper, loading the cut green material onto a cart by hand and fork, then transferring it into the silos, again manually, but green crop loaders, forage harvesters and tractor-mounted handlers all speeded up the process and reduced the physical effort required from the workers.

Sowing grain stayed relatively constant until quite recently. Although Brian Waite had sown clover by broadcasting, grain was always semi-mechanised: 'It was always sowed with a drill – one man on the tractor or with the horse, one on the drill to make sure it flowed through right and one with the cart ready to refill the drill when it was needed.'

The drill itself became gradually more sophisticated in the ways that the seed and, where required, fertiliser, was measured into the ground. Cultivator drills broke up the surface of the soil before applying the seed, then covered it using cultivator tines behind the seed coulters. Direct drills followed, with seed placed into slots cut in the uncultivated soil, with Lincolnshire companies such as John Dale and Simba specialising in reducing the number of times land had to be worked to establish a crop.

In the grain crop, the mower had become the reaper-mower, to be quickly followed by the sail reaper – or side-delivery reaper – which laid the cut crop alongside the machine in bundles suitable for binding into a sheaf. That, in turn, was largely replaced by the binder, which tied the cut grain into a sheaf and dropped it alongside. Some binders even held a number of sheaves on the machine until enough had been accumulated to make a complete stook – a number of sheaves stacked on end side by side to allow the wind to blow through and help them dry. Although binders might seem to have obvious benefits compared to the more basic reapers, they were less effective where the corn had been badly laid by wind or rain, or where there was a high proportion of weeds in the crop. In such cases, as David Creasey remembered, the farmer might prefer to see the crop cut and the weeds allowed to wither and dry out before it was bound into sheaves:

'On the black land before we had good herbicides the weeds always grew well. We had one year when the weather had knocked the wheat down, then all the weeds got tangled into it, the binder just jammed up. We just happened to have a neighbour's old sail reaper in the barn, so we brought it out and did the job – after a fashion!'

John Michael's father was not happy when that happened:

'He hated it when my grandfather insisted on getting out the reaper because the crop was too wet or too green, because he was the one who would have to follow on with cut lengths of twine tying it all up into sheaves.'

The sail reaper still had problems dealing with such crops since the cut corn did not lie neatly ready for tying.

All the machines needed some care to get set up correctly and to continue to run smoothly. Straw is a tough substance to cut, with silica crystals in the stems, so knives had to be sharpened regularly – although Geoff Robinson claimed that he had to sharpen the knives every acre when cutting grass, since the lower setting of the cutter meant that it caught more stones and molehills than when working in corn. There were also lots of grease nipples and lubrication points that needed to be attended to in order to keep everything working smoothly. The binders had another problem.

'The knotters were always difficult. If you kept the fingers clean with a drop of oil, they were usually right, but if they jammed, or the string didn't flow through properly, they didn't tie the sheaf, so all you got was a loose bundle just dropped onto the ground.' [Bryan Marshall]

■ Grass mowing with a Fordson Dexta, the company's rival to the little grey Fergie in the small tractor market. (David Creasey) ■

Another method of keeping the fingers well lubricated was to put a little oil into the centre of each ball of binder twine before fitting it onto the machine.

David Creasey agreed that such problems occurred, but just saw them as part of the job: 'The knotters and such on binders and balers were always a problem, but once you'd worked with them for a while you soon got to know how to deal with them.'

Combine harvesters had been introduced on American farms early in the 19th century, often hauled by substantial teams of horses or mules, but they took nearly 100 years to cross the Atlantic and arrive in Lincolnshire. Part of the reason for the delay was that the American machines were designed to cut corn that was already very dry, a situation rarely achieved under British conditions. Here we cut the corn slightly earlier, and used the practice of stooking to allow the sheaves to dry out before taking them to the stacks. As the new machines came in, harvest was delayed to suit, though not without some qualms on the part of farmers worried that the crop would be more open to damage from wind or rain.

Most of the early combines to be found in the UK came in from the US or Canada, although some local firms, including Clayton and Shuttleworth and Marshalls did produce machines based on their threshing drum technology. However, firms like Massey Harris, Allis-Chalmers or International Harvester had the advantages of scale, speed of development and experience in the field. Massey Harris introduced their MH21 in 1941; the first to arrive in Britain were at work the following year, and by the late 1940s there were more than 1,000 of them in the country. The 21 was a self-propelled machine, which had the advantage of being able to be driven straight into the crop, whereas a trailed unit was offset behind the horses or the tractor and had to have a band round the field cleared by a man with a scythe so the crop would not be trampled on the first circuit. Self-propelled were, however, more expensive to buy, so most of the trans-Atlantic firms offered a choice of self-propelled or tractor-pulled options.

Tony Ireland's father was almost pushed into a rapid expansion of his combine harvester fleet.

'We had had trailed combines before the war, but we were then provided with a Mather and Platt grain dryer under War Ag instructions, along with two Massey 21s to make sure we made best use of it. I think we were drying till nearly Christmas that first year.'

■ *Leading clover with the aid of a green crop loader at Grove Farm, Swaton – Jack Handford and Helmut on the load.*
(Chris Richardson) ■

Tony himself was not allowed to drive the 21s.

'I was only a small boy, and they had a big wheel that you used to lift the bed, and it was too heavy for me to turn.'

Many farmers continued to rely on the older types of equipment well into the 1950s or even the 60s, helped by a claim that merchants buying corn for seed didn't like combine threshed grain because of unspecified damage that might have been done by the process. Tony Hutton's father went to see a recently-arrived combine in the late 1940s, and wasn't impressed. 'It'll never catch on, he said, and went back to his binder.'

■ *A very late user of a threshing machine. John Cook, from Sempringham, working here in 2001, supplies long straw to thatchers. Combine harvesters break the stems too much for that job.* (Brian Lawrance) ■

Michael Read's father was among those who stayed with the older equipment.

'We were still using binders well into the 1950s with all the stooking and stacking that that involved; then we bought a Massey Harris 726, followed by two 780s before going to a Clayson 103. That was one of the first big combines, and one that really did work well.'

Others moved quickly to the new technology. Bob Scarborough's father was convinced by his first experience of seeing a combine at work on his own farm, which appeared to yield better when combined.

'I remember him saying, "We've had fifty hundredweight to the acre here – if we'd cut that with a binder I'd have been satisfied with thirty. There must be something in this combining. I think we'll have to get one of these", which was unusual to hear him

■ *A pair of MF 780 special combines at work on the Long Field at Cranwell in the 1950s. Some of the buildings at the RAF College Cranwell can be seen in the background.* (Tony Ireland) ■

■ A Claas combine driven by 'Joker' on the Scarborough farm at Skellingthorpe. It is unloading into a trailer pulled by a David Brown tractor. Lincoln cathedral can be seen on the hilltop in the background. (Bob Scarborough) ■

wanting to go in for something like that. Part of it was that it wasn't as dry as bindered wheat, but it also wasted a lot less from being shaken out.'

Despite being a big enough farmer to justify owning his own threshing set, George Read was a man who was always keen to be an early adopter of the latest kit. His son, Dick, remembered the International 62 combine that came in a big box from America, to be assembled on the farm.

'We built it in the yard; got it all put together; the mechanic came down from the dealer to make sure it was right and we only then found out that it was too wide to go through the gates – we had to dismantle part of it just to get it out of the yard!'

Most of the early machines had their own idiosyncrasies. David Creasey worked with an Allis-Gleaner in the 1950s:

'It had the drum right behind the bed, which meant that if you got a big stone or something in it, it could do a lot of damage. To avoid that, there was a kind of spring-loaded hatch that would open and drop the stone through, but it didn't close again afterwards, so if you didn't realise it had happened you left a stream of unthreshed corn across the field. You had to stop the machine and get on your back under it to close it up again.'

■ The first user of a combine harvester in Lincolnshire was Geoffrey Henry Neville of Wellingore and Aubourn Hall, who bought the Caterpillar 38 machine seen in this picture. It was probably purchased in 1929, along with the Caterpillar tractor seen hauling it. The young man with his back to the camera is Geoffrey's nephew Henry, later Sir Henry, Nevile, who farmed the estates after the Second World War, and served later as Lord Lieutenant of Lincolnshire. ■

A trailed MH combine at work on Mr Harrison's farm near Lincoln. Motive power provided by the farmer's International Farmall tractor; the combine, supplied by a contractor, had its own engine to drive the mechanisms. (Bob Scarborough) ■

David wasn't impressed with the Allis: 'It had a chain drive, rather than belts, but the chains were not strong enough, so they kept breaking, especially if there was a big crop going through'.

David Bratley acquired a second-hand Minneapolis Moline, which caused him endless problems:

'It was always going wrong, until the time that my father asked one of the men why the combine wasn't working, and where was I? The man replied, "He's inside the old b****r again" but a couple of days later he told me to come and look out the window, where he had something for me. It was a brand new 780, and it was one of the most welcome things I have ever seen!'

Arthur Borrill's farmer's Massey 726 was a reliable machine, but they were concerned about the safety of the driver:

'He sat on top of the petrol tank, which was worrying enough given the tendency of combines to catch fire, but he also smoked a pipe all day, so he was a fire risk all on his own.'

The machine was a bagger, which needed two people to work it, so when the men broke for lunch, Arthur, just 12-years-old, drove the combine, while his father looked after the bagging. A 12-year-old would never be let near the combine driver's seat nowadays, despite the fact that the whole process is probably a lot simpler and safer than it was then.

Ian Clark was not impressed by the stamina of some of the early combines:

'They couldn't stand it – they were always breaking – and they didn't always work the way you wanted them to. The Massey 746 had an electric lift, which was operated by a lever, but when you pushed it, it didn't always move, so you pushed it a bit more and then it came up like a rocket. You didn't want anybody standing in front of it when that happened.'

The later 780, he added, was an improvement, being fitted with a much smoother hydraulic lift.

Michael Lambert dipped his toe rather cautiously into the combine market for a start, but soon found the machines were worth having:

'We bought a little trailed International at first, which was a great little combine, but we soon realised we needed something bigger, so we got ourselves a New Holland.'

Graham Parkinson used a little 4-ft-cut Ransomes – one of the few British-designed machines of its type. The weather made a big difference to its performance:

'In 1958 it was so wet that we had to use two Power Majors to pull it, but the following year it was so dry that one Major could take it, and the only limit to the speed was if you could stay in the seat!'

The early combines could usually be supplied with a choice between a grain tank that held the harvested corn until it could be off-loaded into a trailer, or a bagging platform, where sacks were filled with grain, then slid down a chute into the field to wait to be picked up by a man with a cart. Graham added that the weight of the bags could also vary with the weather:

'In that very dry year, the grains were so small and dry that the bags were holding 23 stone instead of the usual 18. The man who came to collect them in the lorry grumbled a lot about that. Later, when the railways sacks changed from 18 stone to 12, a farmer we were contracting for asked us not to tell his neighbour about the change. He wanted him to think he had had a 50% increase in yield.'

The sack neck had to be tied by a worker standing on the platform, and the need to reduce the cost of sacks and avoid loss of grain meant they had to be well-filled and tightly tied. There was a knack to tying a string round the neck of a filled sack, but there were different ways of doing it. Michael Read described the process:

'You would expect just to wrap the string round and tie it, but you had to do one turn round, then do a half knot, followed by another turn and then tie it properly.'

However, my wife was taught a different method. You doubled the length of string, wrapped it round, then fed the cut ends through the loop and pulled it tight. After doing that, you took the two ends round in opposite directions and tied them, so you effectively had three strings round the neck.

Although the combine reduced the need for labour, it could increase the load on the men who were left on the farm. Brian Waite had a particularly hard experience with a 1972 Claas combine which was nearing the end of its working life. He was in charge of the livestock as well as the combining:

■ *The last year that the binder was solely responsible for the grain harvest at Manor Farm, Blankney Dales, was 1959. A combine was bought in 1960, and although the binder remained in use for some time, the more modern machine gradually took over.* (Left to right) *Ben Diggins, Dave Lincoln, George Leggate, Harry Diggins.* (Sam Leggate) ■

■ *A Hume pea loader pulled by a Fordson Major tractor loading vining peas onto a Commer lorry (owned by Patrick Dean Ltd), near Branston, for transporting to Parker Dean Produce.* (Stuart Hemington) ■

■ *Off-loading vining peas from lorries into static viners on a Tinsley farm near Holbeach.* (H.Tinsley) ■

'I got up at 3 am and put the harvested corn through the dresser and the drier. While that was doing, I dealt with the livestock, then back onto the combine till 10. That Claas finally died in the field, and I very nearly did too. I went down with pneumonia, and that was the end of my working there, because they sold up the following year.'

As well as the grain coming off the combine, there was also the straw. Initially, it was forked loose onto trailers and carted to the yard, either to be stacked or to be fed into static balers. George Read bought a straw walker to help load the straw from the combine onto trailers, but that had its problems as well:

■ *A Shelbourne Reynolds SB 8000 Turbo self-propelled pea viner working on Metheringham Heath for Parker Dean Produce.* (Stuart Hemington) ■

'In 1945 it just left the straw all over the field, so we decided it would be best to burn it, but the minute it got well lit we had half the RAF fire engines in Lincolnshire turning up – they thought a bomber had crashed!'

The following year he bought a baler, which needed two operators at the back feeding in the wires that were used to bind the bales:

'Father looked at those two men, standing in a great cloud of dust, trying to thread those wires into the machine, and he told them to stop using it – it was just too dangerous.'

It was a sensible move; balers could be dangerous machines. George Curtis's uncle lost an arm in one incident, but being dragged into the machine could be fatal. Such lack of concern for health and safety was not unusual for the day and, as Richard Needham pointed out, there was often a reason for it:

'We had an International baler with a Manco engine on top to drive it. When we were pulling it with the old Fordson Major, it was often a job to get both engines started and running, so it was always tempting to try to clear a machine with the engine running, rather than stop it and risk it not starting again.'

Balers, like Richard's father's International, were towed by a tractor, but had to have that extra engine mounted on top to provide enough power for the baler, and to offer it more flexibly. When live PTOs became available in the middle 1950s the power was taken directly from the tractor and that extra engine was no longer needed.

An alternative to the traditional small square bale was the round bale, wrapped with twine – the Roto-baler – produced by Allis Chalmers. It made a bale that was convenient for bedding down stock, but it had its own idiosyncrasies in operation.

'To get it to wrap the bale, you had to stop the tractor, then re-start the PTO which wound the twine round the bale – get the timing wrong and you either had very thin bales or it expanded till it jammed the machine.' [Bob Parker]

Various machines were developed to help load the bales, but most were superseded by the arrival on farm of front-end loaders, which also facilitated the development of much bigger and heavier bales, both square and round. The Howard Big Baler was an early arrival on the UK farming scene, to be swiftly followed by machines and systems produced by New Holland, Hesston and Claas, then by Massey Ferguson and various others. Modern technology now allows a farmer to check and adjust bale weights and sizes, and to tie or wrap them in a variety of materials.

■ *An Allis Chalmers Rotobaler being pulled by an International 275 tractor at Hanthorpe in 1966. The onlookers were students at the Shuttleworth agricultural college who had never seen one before.* (David Creasey) ■

MECHANICAL MARVELS – ROOT CROPS

■ *Potato harvesting with a spinner opening up the rows. Wally Wright working on the tractor at Kirkby Underwood. (David Creasey)* ■

ROOT CROPS SUCH AS SUGAR BEET and potatoes also saw a switch from the gang labour referred to earlier to a more mechanised approach. Potato planting took its first step away from workers dragging crates or baskets of chitted tubers as hand-fed planters became available, usually as attachments for tractor-mounted ridgers. The early machines still required a human hand to drop potatoes down

■ *Jim Young opening out the furrows prior to planting potatoes. A gang of eight women would follow him down the furrows. (Brian Lawrance)* ■

■ *A Ferguson potato planter with chutes down which you dropped a potato each time a bell rang. It is set up for chitted seed, with crates of tubers stacked ready for use – an empty crate had just been dropped behind the machine.*
(Bob Scarborough) ■

a chute on the cue of a ringing bell in the case of a Ferguson machine – 'You could hear that b*****y bell in your bed at the end of the day,' commented Eamonn Sleaford – or to place them into compartments or cups on a belt or rotor which laid them into the furrow. As the technology improved, human involvement on the planter became less and less necessary, and modern implements now only need a driver, who basically guides what is essentially a fully automated procedure.

Potato harvesting saw a similar move from gang labour to full automation, although some of the steps took a while to get right. Moving the trailed potato spinner onto the tractor was an early and fairly straightforward move, but elevator diggers – often referred to as 'hoovers' – lifted the crop from the ground, rattled it up a rod and chain elevator to allow soil and, hopefully, stones to fall through. The

■ *Bob Scarborough's first potato harvester. A Bergmann harvester working at Skellingthorpe, with a team of women removing clods, stones, haulm and damaged tubers before they are loaded into the trailer alongside.* (Bob Scarborough) ■

■ *Waggoner John Coddington on a horse-drawn Blackstone potato spinner on Frank Measures' Major Farm, Hanthorpe in 1957.* (Brian Lawrance) ■

tubers themselves dropped off the back to lie in a neat row ready for the pickers who would be following close behind. Bryan Marshall worked with some of the early machines:

'Just after the war a farmer at Great Hale had a Johnson hoover. It never did work properly, but I did work later with one of the first complete harvesters – a Whitsed, made in Peterborough. It was blacksmith-made, so the parts were sometimes forced together a bit, so if you had to undo anything, it sprang out in all directions.'

That Whitsed machine used an X-ray system to detect stones and clods in the lifted crop, and a system of rubber fingers to remove the unwanted material but, according to Bryan, the detection system was over-enthusiastic, and removed many of the potatoes as well. It was eventually relegated to the more controlled circumstances of the indoor pack-house.

Some of the early harvesters still needed a separate topper to go through the crop, although Bryan commented that it depended on the amount of haulm and whether it had died back or been desiccated with acid to kill it:

'Getting a lot of top through with the potatoes made lifting difficult – they tangled the machines and hid the potatoes in the row, but as long as there wasn't too much or it was very wet, you could usually manage. We always sprayed if we were growing for seed because that stopped the tates from getting too big.'

Those first diggers were developed into complete harvesters by adding a sorting table, at which staff riding on the machine could complete the process of removing stones and other detritus before the

■ *Potatoes being lifted on Tinsley's farms, near Holbeach. Three harvesters, each loading straight into a Muirhill dump truck.* (H. Tinsley) ■

■ *A Nuffield rowcrop tractor pulling a potato harvester. The crop is being sorted on the side elevator before falling into the Muir-Hill dumper.*
(H. Tinsley) ■

■ *Opening a potato grave to allow the crop to be riddled and bagged before being sold. Every bag was weighed before going off the farm, and the two 56lb weights on the scales show that each bag was eight stones – 50kg – twice the usual current weight of a bag in the shops.* (H. Tinsley) ■

■ *A Standen Tornado beet harvester built around a Case skid unit.* (Author's collection) ■

crop passed to a bagging area where it was packed into sacks and tied off. The crop could also be offloaded by another elevator onto a trailer running alongside the harvester.

Mechanisation also came to beet lifting, although Bob Scarborough's first experience was not an encouraging one. His father had bought a two-stage system: one machine to take the green tops off the beet, and another to lift the roots out of the ground:

'The beet lifter worked alright, but it was too heavy for the tractor to pull, and the topper that went before it had a bad habit of digging itself into wet ground, then turning over and hitting the tractor. It just missed me, and after that my father wouldn't let it be used.'

George Read maintained his interest in getting the most up-to-date equipment for his farm in the sugar beet field.

'The regular men didn't like knocking beet, so that was usually done by an Irish gang. We had one of the first Catchpole beet lifters – we saw it at a demonstration at Newark and bought that actual machine. I remember that it had great big wheels, just like steam engine wheels, but I was very little at the time, so it might not have been as big as I recall. It just lifted the beet and dropped them in sort of heaps across the field. There was a device that was supposed to scrape the tops away before dropping them, but it didn't work very well – we still had to have a gang of Irish following on to finish the topping and load the roots.' [Dick Read]

Bryan Marshall worked with a similar machine:

'When I left school in the early 50s we had one of the Catchpoles with a steering wheel. I had a close shave with that one – there was a sort of box at the back into which the roots went, and you dumped them from it into heaps at the side of the row. When it was wet, it all get very sticky, and the beet didn't go through very well. It had all got stuck, so I went to clear it with a stick, but my jacket and boiler suit got tangled up on a sprocket in the drive chain. It ripped my jacket in half and tore the boiler suit off, but I didn't get pulled in, although I was pretty scared at the time.'

The Catchpole also featured a rake that collected up the tops, and Bob Fletcher commented that that was just another thing to have to think about, on top of steering the machine and dumping the roots: 'There was a pedal that you pressed to leave the tops and a lever for the roots, so you had to keep your wits about you.'

The weather has always been a consideration when lifting beet.

'We were working in very dry, hard conditions, with lots of the beet being broken off half way down the root, where all the sugar is, so I told the boss, we could do with some rain. But it was just after grain harvest, and he said I shouldn't wish for rain because there were more people needed it dry than wet. Well, a week or so later, it poured, and we were working ankle-deep in squad, and he came back and said did I still want the rain?!'

■ *One of the earliest successful beet harvesters: the Catchpole topped and lifted a single row of beet. An operator on the harvester kept it lined up on the row.* (Author's collection) ■

■ *One of the noisy options being demonstrated at Caythorpe. The harvested beet from this John Salmon harvester was transported into the holding tank on top of the driver, ensuring a steady rumble and thud to add to the already considerable noise of the tractor and harvester.* (David Creasey) ■

Those early Catchpoles and Standens were soon developed into complete harvesters, with the addition, as with the potato machines, of an elevator to offload the crop into an accompanying trailer. Some carried the lifted crop in a holding tank, which could then be emptied onto a convenient location at the side of a field to wait for onward transport. Tony Hutton commented that when one, a Salmon, was well-loaded it was so heavy that 'you didn't need to have it in gear when lifting downhill'. In that case, the holding tank for the beet was carried on top of the tractor; in another, the Standen Solobeet, one of the early self-propelled single row harvesters, it was just behind the tractor driver's head providing an even noisier environment than the clanging of bells on that potato planter: 'It was like being hit on the head every few seconds until the bin got more full, then it calmed down a bit'. The Solobeet was built around a tractor, which the company offered to collect from the farm, if the buyer didn't want to pay for a new unit, although John Redhead found the machine that he was given to work with was not always up to the job: 'It was built around a Ferguson, and although it would work well when the land was dry, it simply wasn't big enough to do the job in the wet.'

It used a two-stage topping system, with one blade cutting a lot of the green leaf away, so that the second one got a clearer run at the base of the leaves. That second blade threw the tops under the tractor, but could also kick stones free from the row top, giving problems to the driver of any tractor that came up alongside the harvester to collect the lifted roots:

'I've known stones to fly up and smash the windscreen and, if you didn't have a screen, then you needed to be ready to duck!' [Eamonn Sleaford]

The early harvesters were developed into a variety of increasingly sophisticated machines which, between them offered the grower everything from single, two and three-row tractor-hauled units right up to massive six-row harvesters best suited to very large farmers or contractors. Tony Hutton had a one-man system:

'It was a tractor-mounted Gymnast that lifted the row next to the tractor wheel,

■ *Bernard Leggate with a good basketful of potatoes on Blankney Fen.* (Sam Leggate) ■

took it up on a conveyor, cleaned it on the machine, then delivered the cleaned beet back past the other side of the tractor into a one-ton potato box mounted on the front.'

Once the beet was lifted, it still had to be got to the factory. Most now goes by road, but rail and water have had a part to play in the past. Growers close to our home in an old railway station often talk of bringing cart loads into the station yard to be transferred to open wagons. David Bratley found that it could be a race to get the best loading spot at the station: 'It was always easier to load from the cattle dock but, however quick we were, it always seemed that the Irelands got there before us.'

Mary Read's father, Dick Leggate, farming on Blankney Fen, used barges on the River Witham to get the crop to the Bardney factory: 'The men would cart it down to the river bank, and tip it out, after which it had to be loaded into wheelbarrows and taken over a single plank onto the barge.'

The beetroot crop in the north of the county was not quite as complicated as that of sugar beet, since the demand for roots of varying size meant that gapping and singling were not needed. If the buyer wanted a lot of small roots, a thicker stream of seed was drilled; if the demand was for larger ones, less seed went in.

Anthony Hopkins remembered that his grandfather was always keen to make the best use of any bit of land:

'He would always plant right into the corners of the field, so when we went in to lift them with a single row Armer, the women had to go into the corners and pull the beet, twist the top and collect them in a plastic bag, and then dump them from it into the back of the harvester.'

NEW TOOLS

·

ALTHOUGH MUCH OF THE CHANGE over the century was incremental, or saw the replacement of one system with another that was faster or cheaper, there were some significant new ideas, of which the use of crop protection products – those dreaded 'farm chemicals' of popular mythology – was probably the most important.

The use of lime, rock phosphate and other mineral products, along with manufactured nitrogen fertiliser, was already well-established. Implements such as fertiliser spinners, reciprocating plate distributors, star wheels and others were developed to apply such materials. The new pesticides and herbicides, however, needed application systems that allowed small amounts to be applied in a liquid form over large areas. The first such tools were horse-drawn sprayers which applied products like copper sulphate, to help control potato blight, and sulphuric acid, to control weeds or to dessicate crops. Fears that the Germans might try to infect British potato crops with Colorado beetle led to the development of more sophisticated sprayers in the 1940s, which were improved over the years to give the current ranges of self-propelled and

■ *Sid Marwood, of Wickenby (right) and Tom Credland, pictured in 1953 beside a Fordson P6 Major (Perkins), with a Preston Farmers sprayer behind.* (From the Museum of Lincolnshire Life, courtesy of Lincolnshire County Council.) ■

■ *A sprayer mounted on a Fordson Major tractor at Long Sutton in 1955.*
(Peter Piccaver, courtesy Lincolnshire Film Archive.) ■

tractor-drawn machines.

For a while, aerial spraying from aircraft or helicopters was a popular option for some products, although the inability to ensure accurate placement of the active ingredients and to control spray drift has made them less attractive to farmers, and to some farm staff.

'When they were spraying, it was my job to stand at the end of the field to show the pilot where he was supposed to spray. When he started to spray, I had to run out of the way, but I often got a lung-full of goodness know what!' [David Harper]

The introduction of improved weed-killing substance also dramatically reduced the amount of hand-hoeing that had to be done, and the need to leave land fallow – with no crops being grown for a number of months or sometimes a whole year.

Ted Shepherd remembered that, when his family took over a farm near Stallingborough, a requirement of the tenancy was that, each year, a proportion of the land would be fallowed in the summer:

'In those days it was the only way you could clean land – there were not so many chemicals then to kill off the weeds, so you had to do it mechanically. We ploughed it three times, then waited for it to get green all over with weeds, then we cultivated it to loosen the weeds and drag harrowed it several times to heap up the result. The rest we left to the sun and the weather.'

Chris Hodgson, a partner in the now-closed Sleaford Cattle Market, argued that the introduction of crop protection products had had a great effect on the nature of Lincolnshire farming, and the environment:

'Before they came in, everyone worked to a rotation that usually involved some fallowing as grassland, which meant that most people kept livestock – if you drove from Sleaford to Lincoln over the Heath, you saw quite a lot of sheep and cattle. Now that they don't have to fallow, they don't keep livestock, and that has changed farming and the countryside.'

Milking machines had been in existence since the end of the19th century, and had become practical for farm use by the 1920s, but the big switch really only took place in the 1940s and 50s. Not all farmers took to the new equipment.

In 1942, Dickie Hill was one of six Land Army girls milking 100 Ayrshires and three Guernseys near Grimsby, at a farm where a previous owner had tried using machines but had got rid of them:

'We were told that the cows didn't like them, so the farm went back to hand milking. There were three or four men working on a shift system who went in at 4 am to clean out and start the milking. We girls came in at 6 am and had fourteen each to milk, and that took us till about 9.30. It took longer if the cows were difficult. We had one that was a terrible kicker; only the farm manager could milk it.

■ *Dairy farming as the author remembered it. Ten gallon churns being wheeled out ready for collection by the milk lorry.* (Bob Scarborough) ■

■ *Attaching the milking machine cluster to the udder of a Friesian cow.* (Bob Scarborough) ■

Even he needed to have her hobbled on both back and front legs, but she still managed to kick him. We only kept her until after she calved and then she had to go – a pity, because she was a real good milker!'

In 1939 George and Bill Pickwell milked four Lincoln Reds by hand on their smallholding at Moulton, but the expenditure in 1940 of about £90 on two Simplex milking units and the pump to drive them allowed the herd to rise to ten, with some more milky-type cows added to the stock. They later moved to Brant Broughton, where the numbers went up to 30 cows, with the milk going off to Melton Mowbray. The pressure to modernise didn't just come from the farmers' own desire to be more up-to-date; regulation played an increasing part. Bob Scarborough's father was faced with a long list of requirements when he wanted the dairy to become accredited, including a refusal to permit him to wash the milking equipment in the same bath that he and

Bob used for their own personal ablutions! The water supply was also condemned on the grounds, among others that it had 'little wriggly red worms' in it. Installing a mains supply and building a new cow shed and milking parlour were the answer, but they did qualify for a grant for part of the work.

Front loaders mounted on tractors saved a huge amount of hand labour, with the ability to lift and shift loads that would have been too heavy or too inconvenient for men to lift. My father-in-law, Bill Wells-Cole, felt that mechanised handling was a great boon to farming, and Anthony Hopkins, farming on the Isle of Axholme, agreed with him:

'Fertiliser was all in hundredweights and seed corn was always in hundredweights that needed heaving about, and when we did get something in bulk it had to be scooped out to use it, so something that could lift half a ton was one of the best things to have happened in the past 50 years.'

■ *A display of new equipment on show at the Brigg Industries Fair in 1950. Milking machines and electric fencers mixed in with pig wire and milk silos.*
(Peacock and Binnington) ■

■ *New tools did not have to be bought in. Bob Armstrong needed to be able to bring a cow and new-born calf back into the yard, so he built this trolley to carry the calf. The cow followed by instinct. (Bob Armstrong)* ■

Filling muck carts, previously done by men with muck-forks, was something that the early loaders were designed for, and which they usually did well. However, Bob Parker, who worked near Louth in the 50s and 60s, found even they were not perfect:

'We had a Horndraulic on an old Fordson Major which cleared the yard much faster than we could, but if it dropped a big wet load on the back of the cart, it nearly lifted the old horse off the ground. You then had to try to drop a smaller one over it onto the front to get the balance back. Later, when we had a spreader with an augur, a big dry lump didn't always sink down onto the augur so nothing much came out the back!'

Silage needs to be kept free of air to allow it to ferment, either in purpose-built silos of wood, brick or concrete panels, or in sealed ground-level clamps. Dickie Hill was a Land Girl sent out to train farmers in how to make and use silage, but the materials she had to work with in 1942 were less solid that those seen later:

■ *The many uses for a fore-end loader: mucking out a yard; returning an engine after service; and moving a hen-house; all on Grove Farm, Swaton.* (Chris Richardson) ■

■ *Loading bales of hay on Bob Armstrong's farm at Bardney, using a Lincolnshire-built Sanderson Teleporter to lift eight to ten bales at a time.* (Bob Armstrong) ■

■ *Land Army girls filling a silage silo on Lowfields Farm, Bardney. The silo was built up in stages, with a new ring of segments added when the first was filled. The girl in the foreground is filling a watering can with molasses, which was added to the grass to help it ferment. The caravan in the background is where the girls ate and slept. The present owner of the farm, Peter White, remembers, as a child, coming through the gaps in the hedge to watch the girls at work.* (Lincolnshire Echo) ■

■ *Bike calling base! One of Tinsley's foremen with the radio set used to communicate with the farm office at Majors Farm, Holbeach St Marks, in 1952.* (H.Tinsley) ■

'We used wire mesh linked round to form a cylinder, which was then lined with pitch-coated paper to keep it sealed. When we had filled one layer of it, we added another ring of wire, which we linked on top of the first just by twisting the strands together. It would eventually get up to eight or ten feet high. We were working inside it, and the biggest problem was getting out, because you couldn't easily lean a ladder against the wire and paper.'

Another tool that made life easier for livestock farmers was the electric fencer, which proved just as impermeable as a hedge or a conventional wood or wire fence. It also facilitated strip grazing – allowing animals access to a fresh area of a forage crop without letting them loose over the whole field. The fencer unit itself could be moved in a matter of seconds, even moving a whole field fence took much less time than any other kind of enclosure.

'If it wasn't for electric fencers, we would have needed a lot more labour on fencing. One man can go on his own and fence a field in a day without pushing himself too much, which would have taken two men several days to put in a conventional fence and the barbed wire can cause horrific injuries to the stock if they get caught in it. You do get one occasionally that seems to be immune to the shocks, but it has to go straight to market – it doesn't fit the system!' [Bob Scarborough]

POWER APLENTY

■

THE FIRST TRACTORS WERE A GREAT IMPROVEMENT on horses in terms of power availability, but farmers soon found a need for even bigger units. Simply increasing the engine size was one option that was popular, but it had its drawbacks. Bigger engines meant heavier tractors, which were more prone to bog down in British climatic conditions. Steel or 'spud' wheels did a better job, but could not be used on public roads because of the damage they did to the surface. There was also a limit to the amount of power that could be transmitted through either steel or rubber-tyred wheels.

'Spuds were much better for grip until they started to slip but if they did, you soon could be in trouble. It was like sitting on top of a couple of trenching machines – the tractor would be sitting on its belly in a matter of seconds.' [Terry Atkinson]

One solution was to put them on tracks, and crawler tractors were very popular in Lincolnshire. Ironically, the concept was first developed

■ *A 1936 Cleveland Cletrac 46/60 crawler fitted with a Hercules engine for work on Burtt's farm at Dowsby.* (Brian Lawrance) ■

127

■ *Getting the tracks to help the tyres. A Track Marshall giving assistance to a Ford 5000 in a very wet 1968/9 at Kirkby Underwood.* (David Creasey) ■

by a county firm, Richard Hornsby & Sons of Grantham, who built their Chain Tractor in 1905, but was not taken forward by them. Three more locally-built machines, from Clayton & Shuttleworth, Martin and Blackstone were early examples of tracked tractors working in the county, but they soon faced competition from American Cletrac and Holt machines. After the First World War the numbers of imported machines increased as Caterpillar, which had taken over the Holt and Best Tractor brands, International Tractors and Allis Chalmers entered

the market. A home-built machine, the Fowler Gyrotiller, was a tracked machine with what looked like a pair of giant egg-whisks mounted on the back.

In addition to tractors which were built with tracks, there were also machines like the Trackson. This was an early example of what became a fairly common practice, taking a skid unit from a wheeled tractor – in this case, a Fordson – and fitting it with a track system. Roadless, another conversion specialist, fitted tracks in the 1930s to some Lincolnshire-built Marshall tractors, among other types, and it, together with County, Chaseside, Bray and others offered conversions of many makes in the post-war years. Some used a full set of tracks replacing rear and front wheels, steered by running the tracks at different speeds, while others were half-tracks, with the track running round the rear wheel and onto an idler between the front and rear. Another option used the Rotaped system, where the continuous flexible track was replaced by a series of six flat sections, jointed to ensure that at least one was flat on the ground at all times. Steering for the Rotapeds and half-tracks was still by the front wheels.

Tracks remained the best option for heavy pulling in the years after the Second World War, with the experience gained in building tracked military vehicles put to good use in agriculture. Typical examples would be the Vickers Vigor and Vikon machines, based on British tank types,

although the ultimate sword into ploughshare is probably the Sherman tank; stripped of its turret, this worked as a ploughing tractor after the conflict.

A number of American crawler builders established manufacturing bases in the UK after the war, with the International range being one of the best known. Locally, following what was effectively a merger between Marshall tractors and the John Fowler company in Leeds, Field Marshall engines were fitted to Fowler crawlers, and the combinations were sold as Fowlers or as Track-Marshalls.

Tracked vehicles offered better pulling ability, but still suffered from the problem of causing damage to road surfaces. An alternative way of getting better tractive effort was the introduction of four-wheel drive tractors. Initially, they too were largely specialist conversions carried out by companies like Roadless and County, although the

■ *If you think big, you can buy big. Frank Arden ordered 50 new Fordsons straight off the production line in the 1950s. (Meryl Ward)* ■

David Bratley, with his first 4WD tractor, a 1964 Roadless 75. (David Bratley)

■ *A harvest line up in the park on the Coates Hall Estates in the late 1940s. Three Caterpillar 22 crawlers are each pulling a combine. Les Slater is driving the middle one, with Messrs Kirk, Presswood, Credland and Cheetham on the other machines.* (Brian Slater) ■

Essex company of Ernest Doe & Sons took up a local farmer's bright idea. He had taken two Fordson units, removed the front wheels and joined them with an articulated linkage which allowed both units to be driven from one seat at the rear. The result – a machine nearly twenty feet long, with just the original four back wheels – might have been expected to be cumbersome and difficult to steer, but proved to be surprisingly agile, with a very tight turning circle. That manoeuvrability can still be seen at tractor enthusiast gatherings, where a team of Doe articulated tractors performs as 'The Dancing Does'. Initially sold as a Doe Dual Power, the Fordson conversions were later renamed the Doe Dual Drive or Triple D. The concept was later upgraded to the Doe 130 and 150.

■ *A Doe Triple D belonging to contractor William Carter, showing its sharp turning ability in a field at Parkside Farm, Northorpe, near Gainsborough.* (Rob Dickinson) ■

■ *If one tractor doesn't offer enough power, get several! A line-up of David Browns at Grove Farm, Swaton.* (Chris Richardson) ■

John Redhead was very impressed with his Doe:

'It was wonderful – lots of pulling power and great manoeuvrability. With the front unit able to swing through a right angle, it could nearly turn in its own length. If it had a problem, it was that it could pull harder than its own hydraulics could stand, so it tended to break the top link.'

Eventually, most of the major tractor manufacturers developed four-wheel drive machines of their own, and the conversion companies died out or moved over to different products. There has also been a rebirth of the tracked tractor, with very large machines now riding on rubber tracks. They avoid the problems of road damage, but still offer the big advantage of very light ground-pressure 'footprints' for such large machines. The Track Marshall TM200 was an early example, but the system can now be seen on a number of makes, including Caterpillar, Case, Claas and John Deere.

Tony Gent felt that speed and comfort were the best selling points on his 1990s Cat Challenger:

'It allows the tractor to go much faster and utilise its power through speed rather than just lugging power, as the old metal tracked ones do. It also has all the advantages of a quiet cab, hi-fi radio and air-conditioning that you get from modern wheeled tractors, which gives the men a good working environment.'

■ *A John Deere 4020 ploughing at a demonstration at Caythorpe. The 4020, introduced in 1964, was one of the John Deere 'New Generation' range, offering more power from its six-cylinder engine and greater flexibility of fuel and drive systems.* (David Creasey) ■

UNMIXED FARMING

UNTIL AFTER THE SECOND WORLD WAR, as Mary Read, née Leggate, remembers, most Lincolnshire farmers practised mixed farming – crops and livestock: 'We had a bit of everything – sheep, pigs, cattle and chickens – that was how nearly everyone farmed in those days.'

The farm on which Geoff Robinson worked at Sutton on Sea in the 1950s was probably fairly typical of many medium-sized businesses:

'It was about 100 acres, with three men working, using a tractor and two horses. We fattened store cattle and milked 25 cows, using three milking units, and fed them hay made on the farm, carted loose and fed to them in blocks cut from the stack with a stack knife. The top of the stack went to the store cattle, while the better stuff from the middle was used for the dairy cows.'

The Irelands at North Rauceby also went from a very mixed farming operation to a concentration on cereals and beet:

'My grandfather milked a herd of Lincoln Reds, which provided all the milk for Cranwell in its Royal Navy days and RAF, but we went out of milk, and turned the Reds into a single suckler herd. They were then phased out in favour of bought-in Shorthorn cross Hereford heifers which we put to an Angus or Lincoln Red bull at first, then a Charollais by the 1970s. We also kept quite a large flock of sheep – mules crossed to Suffolks – but none of them really paid, so we got rid of all the livestock and reduced our staffing from fifteen or sixteen men to three, which made a huge difference to our costs.' [Tony Ireland]

The same principles applied even on the better arable lands of the Fens. On the Dobbs' farm at West Pinchbeck, already moving towards

■ *Lincoln Red cattle grazing the sea banks alongside the salt marsh.*
(Author's collection) ■

a specialist potato operation, there were still pigs kept for fattening and a couple of Lincoln Red cows to provide milk for the house and beef calves for sale. Store cattle were also bought in to be fattened in a yard before being sold off for slaughter through the local Spalding market. The Pickwell brothers, at Moulton, grew potatoes and vegetables, kept ten sows and litters, and fattened Irish bullocks on Cowbit Wash after taking a cut of grass for hay before putting the stock on it. On their 35 acres they supported the two brothers, two full-time employees and four women, although George's son, Brian, thinks his father's entrepreneurial skills had a lot to do with their success: 'He used to go to Kettering and Leicester with a lorry selling their produce, and it used to be said that George Pickwell could sell what other people couldn't give away!'

The move away from livestock on most farms also saw the end of the

■ *The Christmas fatstock show and sale at Bourne market in 1977. Owner Geoffrey Hyde is leading the animal; local butcher Bill Ewles is in the white coat by the gate.*
(Brian Lawrance) ■

■ *The Spring Fat Pig Sale at Sleaford Cattle Market. The picture was taken shortly after the ending of food rationing in the early 1950s, when the ending of the controls meant better prices for the best animals. The pigs in the pens appear to be Large Whites.* (Chris Hodgson) ■

tradition of taking summer grazing land for cattle on the Lincolnshire Marsh or the Fen edges. The stock would be housed in buildings or yards at the farm during the winter; cows with calves and females going to the bull would stay there through the year; but, in the spring, the drape cows – those that were no longer going to be used for breeding – and animals being fattened for killing, would be driven to the coast for the summer. Michael Read's family's system would have been typical for the period up to and through the Second World War:

'My grandfather had bought about a hundred acres of land near Burgh-le-Marsh, and my father and his brothers would drive the cattle there along the drove roads. They would have gone through Belchford and up onto the Bluestones Heath road – about 40 miles, and it would take them all day to do it. Then, at the end of the summer, the drapes and the three-year olds – they would actually be about two and a half – would be sold through Burgh market, and the rest driven home for the winter.'

Michael's family were fortunate in being within a day's drive of the pasture, others had a longer journey:

'People coming through here on their way to the coast would have had to break the journey somewhere for the night, and when I took the farm there were two small paddocks, fenced and with water, that were used by those herds.'

The system had its advantages for small children during the war, as Mary Leggate remembered:

'We used to take grazing on the dunes near Theddlethorpe and that was how we got a day out at the sea by going down to check the animals. You did have to be careful where you walked since there were defences on the beach and in the dunes. As we were checking the animals it was alright to use the petrol coupons to get there!'

Arthur Borrill's father fattened Irish cattle on his wet lands – carrs – in the Ancholme valley:

'He would go up to York in the spring to buy these big two-year old beasts. They were half wild, but the dealers would run them up the street to show that they were fit, then the deal would be struck just with a spit on the hand and a shake. No paperwork – he just went into the bank branch on the market and told them the money needed to go to Mr So-an-so, and it just happened. He then fattened them on the carr land and sold them at the end of the year.'

Once the carrs were drained, the business moved over to suckler cows and calves housed in the winter and out on grass through the summer, but the business ended when his stockman retired.

■ *An old-style 'bit of everything' farm. Connie Wilson, Ethel ?, Gwen Wilson, Rose and Vi Goddard, with truly free-range poultry on Fir Tree Farm, Eastville 1940s. (From the Museum of Lincolnshire Life, courtesy of Lincolnshire County Council)* ■

■ *A sheep sale in the 1920s at Monks Road, Lincoln.* (From the local studies collection, Lincoln Central Library, courtesy of Lincolnshire County Council.) ■

'I did keep on for a couple of years, but I couldn't do all the work myself and I couldn't find anyone willing to work with them, so I finally got rid of them.'

The lack of labour was a common story, along with the cost of keeping the facilities in good order.

'The crew yards were in poor condition, and the cowman died, so we sold the cattle.' [Hugh Wykes]

Where livestock remained on the farm, it usually moved to a specialised sector. Intensive 'barley' beef was one option, but dairying was another. Bob Scarborough kept his arable side throughout, but

■ *The same market in 1950, again selling sheep, but in smaller numbers. BRS cattle lorries wait for business.* (From the local studies collection, Lincoln Central Library, courtesy of Lincolnshire County Council.) ■

■ *Sam Leggate burning straw on his farm on Thorpe Tilney Fen. Burning off surplus straw after the harvest was banned in 1989, following complaints about smuts on washing and reduced visibility on roads.* (Sam Leggate) ■

streamlined the livestock into his milking herd:

'In the 60s, when father died, sheep had just gone – only just – pigs, chickens, you name it we had it and I realised that I couldn't farm properly doing everything, and I decided that if I got rid of the pigs and had another seven or eight cows we would hardly know they were there, but they would bring in as much income as the pigs, with a lot less work, so we invested in a parlour as well and that has proved to be the right choice.'

The reduction in the number of farmers keeping smaller herds or flocks contributed to the decline of livestock markets in the county – there is now only one, at Louth, with another at Newark just over the boundary, where once there was nearer a score. A farmer needing to sell a couple of beasts or a few sheep found the local market to be the best outlet, but anyone producing larger numbers often found that selling direct to the meat trade was a more efficient way to go. Chris Hodgson, a partner in the now-closed Sleaford market saw 'the move from rotational farming, and related livestock fattening and production, to large scale arable farming in this area' as a major factor in the decline of the market, alongside the increasing use of direct buying by the larger customers and the closure of the local slaughterhouse. The market auctioneers, Earl and Lawrence did try bringing stock in from outside the area, but found that to be uneconomic. 'With the benefit of hindsight, the end was inevitable,' he concluded.

The decline of mixed farming also had the effect of reducing the need for straw to be kept for use on the farm. Although George Read had been unusual in setting fire to the straw in his field in 1945, it became a more regular practice in later years. Farmers argued that it helped keep weeds under control and reduced the carry-over of diseases from one year to the next. Neighbours complained about the effect of smoke and smuts on their lives and their washing lines, and road users objected to the dense clouds that could obstruct their vision. Ironically, it could be that other farmers could get caught in the smoke. I have a letter addressed to a Branston farmer whose lorry ran into that owned by another local landowner in the smoke generated by a third burning his straw. The letter was sent in the hope that damages could be won from the burner, but I have no idea if the claim was successful!

The trend towards specialism shows every sign of continuing into the future. As farmers face up to the demands of massive buyers wanting to pay lower prices for higher-quality goods, the ones most likely to succeed are those who know their own jobs inside out, whether that be as a cereal grower on a couple of thousand acres supplying the commodity or a flower grower with just a few maintaining a specialist niche. The old-style mixed farm of livestock, pasture, roots and cereals appears to be a thing of the past, unless, of course, the economics of fertiliser and energy costs make it profitable again. The future will almost certainly continue to surprise us.

———————■———————

BIBLIOGRAPHY

■

From Plough to College, Joseph H. Smith
  (Richard Kay Publications, 1993)

Country Voices, Charles Kightly (Thames and Hudson, 1984)

Fifty Years of Farm Machinery, Brian Bell (Farming Press, 1993)

Modern Farming, edited by S. G. Brade-Birks (Waverley Book Co,1950)

The Oldest Young Farmer, Reg Dobbs (Sutton Publishing, 2007),
  by Len Woodhead Japonica Press 2003 *A Lincolnshire Lad Looks Back*

A Lincolnshire Lad's Scrapbook, Len Woodhead (Japonica Press, 2008)

O Boy!, Bob Scarborough (self-published, 2005)

Ploughs, Chaff Cutters and Steam Engines, edited by Ken Redmore
  (Lincolnshire Society for History and Archaeology, 2007)

Lincolnshire Potato Railways, Stuart Squires
  (Oakwood Press, revised 2007)

Tractors at Work 1904 – 1994 (Stuart Gibbard Farming Press, 1994)

Tractors at Work, Vol.2 (Stuart Gibbard Farming Press, 1995)

■

INDEX